COMPREHENSION
NINJA
FOR AGES 9–10

ANDREW JENNINGS

BLOOMSBURY EDUCATION
LONDON OXFORD NEW YORK NEW DELHI SYDNEY

11130

BLOOMSBURY EDUCATION
Bloomsbury Publishing Plc
50 Bedford Square, London, WC1B 3DP, UK

BLOOMSBURY, BLOOMSBURY EDUCATION and the Diana logo are trademarks of
Bloomsbury Publishing Plc

First published in Great Britain, 2020 by Bloomsbury Publishing Plc
Text copyright © Andrew Jennings, 2020

Ninja illustrations copyright © Andrew Jennings, 2020
Illustrations copyright pages 28, 39, 59, 78, 88, 99, 118, 129, 132, 133, 140, 149, 156,
165, 168, 172 © Ilias Arahovitis, 2020
Illustrations copyright pages 9, 18, 49, 129, 136, 145, 160 © Daniel Limon, 2020

A catalogue record for this book is available from the British Library

ISBN: PB: 978-1-4729-6926-2

2 4 6 8 10 9 7 5 3 1

Text design by Marcus Duck Design

Printed and bound in the UK by Ashford Colour Press

MIX
Paper from
responsible sources
FSC® C011748
FSC
www.fsc.org

To find out more about our authors and books visit www.bloomsbury.com and sign up for
our newsletters

Acknowledgements

To Christopher Hole, thank you for the inexhaustible level of quality you have brought to the
Comprehension Ninja series and beyond. Your subject knowledge, skills and experience have
been essential in developing the highest quality non-fiction texts, that are engaging, inspiring
and informative for the reader.

CONTENTS

ALSO AVAILABLE FROM ANDREW JENNINGS

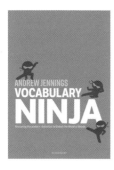

VOCABULARY NINJA

Vocabulary Ninja is an essential toolkit of strategies and resources to supercharge primary pupils and transform them into vocabulary ninjas! This practical book features theory, teaching approaches and photocopiable activities, as well as key topic vocabulary, etymology and phrases to bring the primary curriculum to life.

Go to www.vocabularyninja.co.uk and visit the book section to find out more.

You can find even more information about Vocabulary Ninja here:
Website – www.vocabularyninja.co.uk
Blog – vocabularyninja.wordpress.com
Twitter – @VocabularyNinja
Twitter – @MrJenningsA

SENTENCE SAMURAI

A unique whole-school modeling tool for writing and sentence construction. The app models the expansion of basic sentences to more complex and detailed ones. Each set of sentences has been carefully written to match the National Curriculum's writing requirements and expectations of each year group – Year 1 through to Year 6 in one app!

For more information, see:
Website – www.sentencesamurai.co.uk
Twitter – @SentenceSamurai

VOCABULARY NINJA WORD OF THE DAY APP

A new Word of the Day is released every day! You can get the Word of the Day straight to your smartphone or tablet, making Word of the Day even more accessible on the go or in school. It's perfect for supporting your immersive classroom environment, where every word counts.

VOCAB LAB APP

The Vocab Lab app offers an exciting and engaging way for pupils to explore vocabulary and the possible alternatives for common vocabulary choices. The app contains over 600 alternatives, supported by a child-friendly layout, and has been downloaded over 150,000 times. Simply visit the App Store on your iPad™, search for 'Vocab Lab' and download the app for free.

INTRODUCTION

Comprehension Ninja is designed to be a core part of your arsenal for teaching reading comprehension skills. *Comprehension Ninja* specifically focuses on the retrieval of information, using eight core comprehension skills that underpin the reading domains set out by the National Curriculum. This book contains 24 non-fiction texts that align themselves to the primary National Curriculum, the corresponding foundation subjects and subsequent topics taught within them. As the new curriculum develops, a greater focus has been placed on how pupils retain the knowledge they have learned within all lessons. *Comprehension Ninja* will allow schools to further embed reading opportunities across the curriculum while reinforcing the retention of pupil knowledge via the eight skills found below.

High-quality retrieval skills are the foundation of reading comprehension. If pupils can effectively and efficiently locate and retrieve information, then from there, inference, sequencing and explanation-type questions can be accessed. Without being able to retrieve information, none of this is possible. Many years ago, before SATs, these skills were known as comprehension skills! Now, sadly, they are known as question types. But the key principles still apply – and the eight skills below need to be taught, practised and mastered.

 **Labelling**   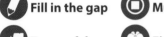 **Matching**

Fill in the gap   **Multiple choice**

True or false   **Find and copy**

123 Sequencing   **Underline or highlight**

Most comprehension texts bombard pupils with a range of question types that they have not yet had time to master – meaning they quickly encounter questions they cannot answer. *Comprehension Ninja* places the emphasis on teachers to teach and model each skill, while pupils develop their understanding of each question type individually.

HOW TO USE THIS BOOK

This book contains 24 non-fiction texts for you to use in your classroom. Texts 1 to 12 have eight subsequent pages of questions built around each comprehension skill. These texts and questions have been created so that you can specifically target and teach each individual skill, and then have a plethora of questions for pupils to work on and answer. In maths, you wouldn't jump from division one day into 3D shapes the next. The same must apply to reading – we should teach each skill and give pupils the opportunities to practise and master these skills before we move on. You now have in your hands 12 texts and associated questions to teach each skill – that's a minimum of 96 lessons from the first 12 texts.

Texts 13 to 24 look more like a traditional test. Each text has a corresponding set of questions. Each set of questions requires the pupil to use the comprehension skills mastered

from texts 1 to 12. You could choose to use these texts formatively across the year to inform which skills require further attention, but here lies a fantastic opportunity for pupils to apply their new skills to each question type independently and with confidence. Don't allow pupils to flounder: if they require support, give it – teach!

It is important to note that this resource hasn't been designed to be a testing tool, but rather a teaching and learning tool. A tool where teachers support pupils to access texts and to master the eight comprehension skills. However, because of the nature of testing in schools, it is important that children see and experience test-type texts and questions as they will from texts 13 through 24. Because of the versatility of this resource, it really is up to you how it is used. Plus, as pupils grow in confidence and skill level, they will relish completing these activities.

PROGRESSION AND DEVELOPMENT OF SKILLS

Normally, teachers and leadership teams love to see a polished skill development matrix that shows how each skill becomes more complex as the pupil learns and grows. The way that *Comprehension Ninja* grows in difficulty is via the complexity and length of the texts. The vocabulary in the book for ages 7–8 is more challenging than the vocabulary in the book for ages 5–6, for example. Some texts will include statutory words from the National Curriculum, plus a range of technical vocabulary related to each different subject. The length of texts that pupils are exposed to falls in line with statutory assessments at Year 2 and Year 6, growing in increments each year, thus increasing the demands on the pupil to retrieve information with accuracy and speed from larger and more complex texts.

Approximate text length progression in the *Comprehension Ninja* series:

Ages 5-6:   100-150 words
Ages 6-7:   200-250 words
Ages 7-8:   300-450 words
Ages 8-9:   500-600 words
Ages 9-10:   650-700 words
Ages 10-11:   700-800 words

PRE-READING AND KEY INFORMATION TO IDENTIFY IN THE TEXT

Ideally, before answering questions, we want to teach pupils to pre-read a text and identify key information in the text.

Pupils need to adopt a positive reading position, sat up straight and ready to read. Prompt children to read with their pencil, so they move it across the page underneath each line as they read it. This means that when it comes to underlining a key piece of information, their pencil is already in the correct location – it's efficient. If pupils need to look away from the text to pick up the pencil, they will need to relocate the key information and time will be lost in every instance they perform this inefficient action.

We often ask pupils to underline key information as they read, but what is this key information?

Names of people, places, companies, events, teams, etc.

Dates including days, months, years, times and periods of time from beginning to end.

Statistics and numbers including percentages, fractions, amounts, figures, etc.

Unknown vocabulary – words pupils don't understand. Identifying them may still help pupils answer a question.

Headings, subheadings and images help direct readers to the correct area of the text when answering a question.

As pupils read through the text with their pencils, we want to train them to underline these pieces of key information. A good guideline as to how much to underline is three to six pieces per paragraph. Key information should be single words, or small groups of words, not full sentences. Model this skill to pupils and discuss why you have underlined this information, referring back to the information above.

KEYWORDS IN THE QUESTION

Once we have read the text and underlined key information, we can begin to answer questions about it. We now need to teach pupils to spot the keyword or phrase in a question. This is a word or phrase that signposts where to look in the text to find the answer. In the example question below, the keyword or phrase is **Morse code**.

*How did soldiers effectively use **Morse code** during World War II?*

If pupils have pre-read the text effectively, Morse code should be underlined, or they may even remember where it is mentioned. Pupils would skim (see below) the text to find the paragraph in which Morse code is mentioned, then scan that section for the exact word or phrase. Once located, pupils should be trained to read the sentence that comes before and the sentence after the one that contains the keyword or phrase. Doing this will give pupils a much greater chance of answering successfully.

In the example question, 'soldiers' or 'World War II' are not the keyword or phrase as it is likely that they would be mentioned numerous times throughout the text and would not help the reader locate the answer.

This is another instance where underlining unknown vocabulary could be effective. Pupils may not understand what Morse code is. However, they can see that it is a proper noun and should underline it when pre-reading as it is a name and unknown vocabulary. They can still answer the question correctly and receive a mark by efficiently locating the information and reading around the keyword, even though they may have no understanding of what Morse code actually is.

SKIMMING AND SCANNING

To be a good retriever of information, pupils must be able to locate information quickly. By skimming and scanning a text efficiently and methodically, pupils will have a much higher chance of locating the information they require.

It's crucial to agree a shared language amongst staff as to what skimming and scanning is. We don't want to use the phrase 'skimming and scanning' without everyone, including pupils, being very clear on what this means.

Skimming is a whole text process. Pupils skim across the text to locate a specific paragraph or area where the required information is likely to be. Skimming is like looking at the chapters of a DVD and choosing which one to start from. We won't necessarily find the answer when skimming, but we hope to locate the correct area of the text.

When asking pupils to skim the text to find the correct area, try asking them to remember first whether the information was in the beginning, the middle or the end of the text. Is there an image or a subheading that can help them skim the text? These strategies can help signpost pupils to the correct area of the text, thus increasing their chances of being successful in answering the question.

Scanning is then looking at that specific section with a greater level of scrutiny, possibly looking for a keyword or phrase. Following the film example, this is like watching a specific film chapter to locate the required information.

> **NINJA NOTES**
>
> Introduce skimming and scanning with images, timetables, TV schedules, poems, lists, visual instructions, hidden word pictures. Ask pupils to locate specific items, objects and information – add a time limit to increase the fun factor.

LABEL / DRAW AND LABEL

Labelling asks pupils to look at an image and label parts of the image with a word from a word bank. As the skill develops, pupils will be asked to label statements with information retrieved from across a whole text. Identifying keywords in the statement or question is essential here.

Draw and label requires pupils to draw an image based on the information they have read and then to label it. The quality of the drawing here isn't necessarily important, focus on the accuracy of the retrieved labels.

> **NINJA NOTES**
>
> Increase the difficulty of labelling by asking pupils to label more complex images without a word bank, but a short paragraph of text. Alternatively, use draw and label as part of your literacy lessons – read and share small yet detailed parts of the book you are using as part of your unit of work. For a task, ask pupils to draw what the text describes, then add labels. Share and discuss the differences in pupils' work and examples of effective labelling.

MATCHING

Matching is a simple skill where pupils are required to match together pieces of information that are in a jumbled state. Pupils must match the information together by drawing lines to the associated pieces of information. The activity becomes more challenging as pupils have a greater number of possible statements to match and larger texts to refer to in order to confirm the match.

Ask pupils to identify the keyword in each statement and then locate this in the text by skimming and scanning. Matching pair games are a great way of introducing this skill to younger pupils. Older pupils might benefit from this skill as part of a starter in foundation subject lessons. They could match information associated with the topic on cut up pieces of paper, thus embedding reading skills and providing an opportunity for pupils to demonstrate foundation subject knowledge.

FILL IN THE GAP

Pupils are given a sentence with a missing word. Pupils will need to locate this sentence in the text and identify the missing word. This skill becomes progressively more difficult as the amount of text increases and as the pupils are given fewer options to choose from.

Practise this skill regularly by giving pupils a page of their reading book and the same page with multiple words blanked out. Prompt pupils to spot keywords in each sentence to locate the specific sentences efficiently.

MULTIPLE CHOICE

These questions require pupils to choose an answer from a selection of three or four possible answers. Prompt pupils to locate the required information by spotting keywords in the question and locating them in the text, then reading around this information to find the correct answer.

Train pupils via discussion to discount illogical answers using what they already know from the pre-read of the text. Also ensure that pupils don't answer questions using their own knowledge of the subject. Prompt pupils to 'prove it' by showing where the exact information is found in the text. This type of question could also be played in the style of a 'Who Wants to Be a Millionaire?' or 'Million Pound Drop' game, where pupils have multiple answers to choose from based on a text of your own choice.

TRUE OR FALSE

Pupils will be given a statement and asked if it is true or false. Younger year groups will begin to learn this skill by answering yes or no, before progressing to true or false.

Ensure pupils are not guessing. Train pupils to spot the keyword in the question and locate this information in the text. By reading around this information, pupils will be able to discover whether the statement is true or false.

123 SEQUENCING

These questions require pupils to sequence information in the order it occurs in the text, from first to last. Younger pupils order the words in single sentences, progressing to pupils ordering information from across a whole text.

Teach pupils to allocate each word or statement (usually no more than five) a symbol – a square, a triangle, a rectangle, a star and a cross. Pupils should then find these statements in the text and mark the corresponding symbol on the text. Once pupils have done this, it is easy to look at the text and see which symbol comes first, second, third and so on. A very effective strategy to help pupils effectively sequence information.

FIND AND COPY

These word-level questions require pupils to identify a word when provided with a contextual description rather than a contextless definition. Pupils will need to use keywords to locate the correct area of the text and then find and copy the correct word. In answering these questions, pupils may need to use a small amount of inference. Pupils may be directed to a certain part of the text at the beginning of the question, e.g. *Look at the paragraph beginning 'These word-level questions…'.*

Example: Look at the paragraph beginning *'The voyage aboard'.* Find and copy a word that suggests that the animals Darwin collected had been dead for millions of years. Answer: fossil.

This skill is much more challenging than its name suggests. Teach pupils to follow the instructional part of the question to locate the correct area of the text efficiently. Although counterintuitive, teaching pupils to apply a 'best guess' approach if they are struggling to find the correct word is still a worthwhile strategy and will more often than not produce a correct answer.

UNDERLINE OR HIGHLIGHT

This skill requires pupils to locate words based on an explicit definition of the word. Pupils may be required to underline words from a single sentence or from a chosen paragraph of the text.

Regularly discuss definitions, play matching games where pupils match words and definitions, and apply the 'best guess' strategy where pupils answer with their own logic without necessarily knowing the answer for certain. Teach Vocabulary Ninja's Word of the Day every day and be sure to explore definitions. Give pupils increasingly difficult words and ask them to create a definition of the word without using the word itself. You can also encourage them to start the definition with 'If someone is…' or 'If something is…'.

1 FAIR TRADE

What is fair trade?

To understand the meaning of fair trade, we can look at each word: 'fair' means 'equal and without discrimination' and 'trade' is the action of buying and selling goods. By putting them together, we can begin to understand that fair trade is about ensuring everyone in the world is treated in the same way when it comes to buying and selling goods. Unfortunately, this isn't always the case.

Why do we need to address fair trade?

Fair trade focuses on producers in 'developing' countries: countries with economies that are weaker than average and have a high need to sell their products. Historically, farmers in developing countries haven't been paid the same as those in developed countries.

As a consequence, farmers don't always make enough money to live – even though they have worked day and night to produce a high-quality product. Large companies exploit farmers' and workers' need to sell, making a huge profit and passing none of it to their suppliers.

What does fair trade achieve?

The fair trade movement aims to ensure that producers are paid a price that is never below the world value of their product. This should allow producers to keep their businesses running.

In this way, fair trade aims to enable even the poorest farmers to feed their families, drink clean water, clothe their children and buy medicines when needed. This may allow them to develop their businesses and their communities, too.

As of 2019, more than 1.66 million farmers and workers are fair trade certified, and there are 1,411 certified producers in 73 countries across the world. In 2016, $158.3 million was paid to these fair trade producers.

Comprehension Ninja 9–10 © Andrew Jennings, 2020

The fair trade of coffee

One of the fair trade movement's priorities is the trade of coffee. Coffee is one of the world's most popular drinks, and its sale is extremely profitable. The cost of producing it is low, and the price of coffee to customers is high.

Coffee is made from small beans that are roasted and ground down into a powder or granules. The beans are actually berries – they come from trees called 'coffea'. It's only after they're dried that they're called beans.

The origins of coffee can be traced back centuries to ancient coffea forests in Ethiopia. Legend says the goat herder Kaldi first discovered their potential after noticing that his goats became energetic after eating coffea berries. Monasteries started making them into a drink that kept them alert during evening prayer. From there, word moved east and coffee became popular across the globe.

Nearly all of the world's coffee is now grown in a region called the 'coffee belt', which is close to the equator. It includes India and Indonesia, and much of Africa and South America. Soil there is rich in nutrients, and the climate is warm and wet – perfect for growing coffea plants. Many countries in the coffee belt are classed as 'developing' countries.

Nowadays, small farms produce 80 per cent of the world's coffee, and it's estimated that 125 million people rely on the coffee trade for their livelihoods. Without the simple coffee bean, millions of people would be without work.

How can we support fair trade?

The most important thing you and your family can do is to buy fair trade products. Keep an eye out for the Fairtrade Foundation's circular green, black and blue logo on packaging. It can be seen on lots of products, including coffee. This logo informs the consumer that the producer of the product is guaranteed to receive a fair price.

FILL IN THE GAP

Read the sentences and choose the correct word or words to fill the gap.

To understand the meaning of fair trade, we can look at each word: 'fair' means 'equal and without _____' and 'trade' is the action of buying and selling goods.

By putting them together, we can begin to understand that fair trade is about ensuring everyone in the world is _____ in the same way when it comes to buying and selling goods.

Fair trade focuses on producers in '_____' countries.

As a _____, farmers don't always make enough money to live – even though they have worked day and night to produce a high-quality product.

Large companies _____ farmers' and workers' need to sell, making a huge profit and passing none of it to their suppliers.

The fair trade movement aims to ensure that _____ are paid a price that is never below the world value of their product.

This should allow producers to keep their _____ running.

In this way, fair trade aims to enable even the poorest farmers to feed their families, drink _____ water, clothe their children and buy medicines when needed.

The beans are actually berries. They come from trees called '_____'.

Legend says the goat herder _____ first discovered their potential after noticing that his goats became energetic after eating coffea berries.

_____ started making them into a drink that kept them alert during evening prayer.

Soil there is rich with nutrients, and the _____ is warm and wet.

Nowadays, small farms produce _____ of the world's coffee.

Without the simple coffee bean, _____ of people would be without work.

The most important thing you and your family can do is to buy _____ products.

 MATCHING

Draw a line with a ruler to match the information.

fair trade focuses on	Kaldi
number of certified producers	'developing' countries
goat herder	coffee belt
close to the equator	1,411

farmers don't have enough	exploit farmers
large companies	the coffee belt
coffee growing region	everyone treated the same
fair trade ensures	money

paid to fair trade producers	guarantee the producer has been paid a fair price
Fairtrade Foundation logo	a tree
coffee	a very popular drink
coffea	$158.3 million

trade means	equal and without discrimination
Fairtrade Foundation logo	73
fair means	buying and selling goods
fair trade countries	green, black and blue

1.66 million	coffea berries
energetic goats ate	clothes, food and medicines
small farms produce	fair trade certified farmers and workers
farmers use money for	80 per cent of the world's coffee

 LABEL

Label the statements with the correct information.

coffee bean tree	
berries become	
region coffee is grown	
legendary goat herder	
one of the world's most popular drinks	
trade means	

Label the statements with the correct information.

farmers and workers were being	
fair trade ensures	
fair trade allows producers	
close to the equator	
roasted and ground down	
equal and without discrimination	

Label the statements with the correct information.

number of certified fair trade workers	
many coffee belt countries are classed as	
paid to producers in 2016	
extremely profitable	
number of countries with certified producers	
guarantees producers an agreed fair price	

 **FAIR TRADE**

 **TRUE OR FALSE**

Read the sentences. Put a tick in the correct box to show which sentences are *true* and which are *false*.

Fair means to be treated equally.   True ☐   False ☐

Trade means the action of buying and selling.   True ☐   False ☐

It is always the case that people are treated in the same way.   True ☐   False ☐

Poor and rich countries' farmers will be paid the same.   True ☐   False ☐

Fair trade focuses on producers in 'developed' countries.   True ☐   False ☐

Fair trade protects farmers from being exploited.   True ☐   False ☐

Fair trade aims to help even the poorest farmers.   True ☐   False ☐

Large companies pass their profits on to their supplier.   True ☐   False ☐

Fair trade allows farmers to feed and clothe their families.   True ☐   False ☐

Fair trade allows farmers to sell their businesses.   True ☐   False ☐

Coffee is one of the world's most popular drinks.   True ☐   False ☐

Coffee is produced from a leaf.   True ☐   False ☐

Coffee comes from a tree called coffea.   True ☐   False ☐

Nearly all of the world's coffee is grown in factories.   True ☐   False ☐

The coffee belt is close to the equator.   True ☐   False ☐

Coffee became popular across the globe when word moved west.   True ☐   False ☐

Small farms produce 100 per cent of the world's coffee.   True ☐   False ☐

Monasteries made a drink with the berries of the coffea tree.   True ☐   False ☐

Kodi the cow herder discovered the coffee bean.   True ☐   False ☐

The Fairtrade Foundation logo is on all products.   True ☐   False ☐

◉ MULTIPLE CHOICE

Circle the correct answer for each of the following questions.

What does the word 'fair' mean?

| everyone is equal | everyone is different | everyone is treated the same | everyone knows the same |

What does the word 'trade' mean?

| buying and selling goods | a market | the same products | giving away your product |

Where is most coffee produced?

| India, Indonesia, Africa and South America | Japan | London, England | North America |

What is coffee made from?

| a cactus | a plant | an animal | a tree |

Before fair trade, farmers were being…

| harmed | exploited | cheated | bullied |

Fair trade was introduced to ensure profits were shared with…

| producers | sellers | large companies | investors |

What are coffee beans turned into?

| liquid | berries | powder or granules | tea |

What is the name of the plant that produces coffee?

| coffea | coffee | cofea | cofee |

What is the name of the region that produces most of the world's coffee?

| the coffee centre | the coffee equator | the coffee lands | the coffee belt |

What shape is the Fairtrade Foundation's logo?

| a square | a triangle | a hexagon | a circle |

123 SEQUENCING

Look at *Fair trade*. Number the statements from 1 to 5 to show the order they occur in the text. Look at the first line of each paragraph to help you.

Fair trade focuses on producers in 'developing' countries: countries with economies that are weaker than average and have a high need to sell their products. ☐

One of the fair trade movement's priorities is the trade of coffee. ☐

The fair trade movement aims to ensure that producers are paid a price that is never below the world value of their product. ☐

Nowadays, small farms produce 80 per cent of the world's coffee, and it's estimated that 125 million people rely on the coffee trade for their livelihoods. ☐

The origins of coffee can be traced back centuries to the ancient coffea forests in Ethiopia. ☐

Look at the last two paragraphs in *Fair trade*. Number the statements from 1 to 5 to show the order they occur in the text.

Without the simple coffee bean, millions of people would be without work. ☐

This logo informs the consumer that the producer of the product is guaranteed a fair price. ☐

The most important thing you and your family can do is to buy fair trade products. ☐

It can be seen on lots of products, including coffee. ☐

Nowadays, small farms produce 80 per cent of the world's coffee, and it's estimated that 125 million people rely on the coffee trade for their livelihoods. ☐

Look at *Fair trade*. Number the statements from 1 to 5 to show the order they occur in the text.

Large companies exploit farmers' and workers' need to sell, making a huge profit and passing none of it to their suppliers. ☐

Historically, farmers in developing countries haven't been paid the same as those in developed countries. ☐

As of 2019, more than 1.66 million farmers and workers are fair trade certified, and there are 1,411 certified producers in 73 countries across the world. ☐

Legend says the goat herder Kaldi first discovered their potential after noticing that his goats became energetic after eating coffea berries. ☐

Coffee is one of the world's most popular drinks, and its sale is extremely profitable. ☐

 FIND AND COPY

These questions are about *Fair trade*.

Look at paragraph one. Find and copy a word that suggests that people should be treated the same.

_____

Look at the 'Why do we need to address fair trade?' section. Find and copy a word that suggests that some countries are not as rich as others.

_____

Look at the 'What does fair trade achieve?' section. Find and copy a word that suggests that fair trade helps to develop the locations where people live, as well as the business.

_____

Look at the 'The fair trade of coffee' section. Find and copy a word that suggests that coffee can make companies huge amounts of money.

_____

Look at the paragraph beginning 'Coffee is made from…'. Find and copy a word that suggests that coffee beans are crushed.

_____

Look at the paragraph beginning 'The origins of coffee…'. Find and copy a word suggests that coffee beans had something to offer that no one has realised.

_____

Look at the paragraph beginning 'Nearly all of the world's coffee…'. Find and copy a word that suggests that coffee is best grown around the central line of the Earth.

_____

 Comprehension Ninja 9–10 © Andrew Jennings, 2020

UNDERLINE OR HIGHLIGHT

Read the paragraphs below and then follow the instructions.

Coffee is made from small beans that are roasted and ground down into a powder or granules. The beans are actually berries – they come from trees called 'coffea'. It's only after they're dried that they're called beans.

The origins of coffee can be traced back centuries to the ancient coffea forests in Ethiopia. Legend says the goat herder Kaldi first discovered their potential after noticing that his goats became energetic after eating coffea berries. Monasteries starting making them into a drink that kept them alert during evening prayer. From there, word moved east and coffee became popular across the globe.

Nearly all of the world's coffee is now grown in a region called the 'coffee belt', which is close to the equator. It includes India and Indonesia, and much of Africa and South America. Soil there is rich in nutrients, and the climate is warm and wet – perfect for growing coffea plants. Many countries in the coffee belt are classed as developing countries.

Underline or highlight a word that means to find out how something starts or begins.

Underline or highlight a word that means belonging to the distant past.

Underline or highlight a word that means being aware of something.

Underline or highlight a word that means enjoyed or liked by a lot of people.

Underline or highlight a word that means that a substance contains a lot of something.

Underline or highlight a word that means able to pay full attention.

2 MOUNTAINS OF THE WORLD

Huge and often striking, mountains can be found all over the world. They create picturesque backdrops and provide extreme sports enthusiasts with climbing, trekking and skiing opportunities – but what are they, exactly?

Mountains are areas of land that are higher than the land around them, but different definitions based on height exist. In Great Britain, the government's definition is a summit of 600 metres or higher. However, mountains can rise to thousands of metres in height.

Mountains are created by areas of Earth's solid crust, called 'tectonic plates', moving on the liquid magma beneath them. Some are made when plates push together and force the ground up where they meet. Some are created by magma erupting from gaps between the plates. Others have been created by underwater volcanoes, when lava reaches the surface.

A group of mountains together is known as a mountain range. Some of the world's best-known ranges include the Alps in Europe, the Rocky Mountains in North America and the Himalayas in Asia. Some of the world's best-known mountains – although not all the highest – are Everest, Kilimanjaro, Fuji and Vesuvius.

Everest

Undoubtedly the most famous mountain of them all, Everest is in the Himalayas in Asia. It is the highest mountain in the world, at a staggering 8,848 metres tall.

Many adventurous climbing enthusiasts have attempted to climb it. At times, it can be so busy that queues form along the route to the summit. Over 5,000 brave climbers are said to have reached the top, but nearly 300 have died during their attempts.

Climbing Everest requires intensive training and can cost a lot of money. Many climbers take on the challenge in order to raise funds for charities.

Comprehension Ninja 9–10 © Andrew Jennings, 2020

Kilimanjaro

Kilimanjaro is Africa's highest mountain. It is located on the northern border of Tanzania, overlooking Kenya. Its summit rises to 5,895 metres – almost 3,000 metres lower than Everest's. Despite its location, its peak is covered with snow and ice all year.

Kilimanjaro is made up of three inactive volcanoes: Kibo, Mawensi and Shira. Shira is the oldest peak. Kibo is the youngest and had the most recent major eruption – but that was around 360,000 years ago.

Fuji

Fuji, the highest mountain in Japan, is 3,776 metres tall. It is situated to the west of the capital city of Tokyo. Fuji is a volcano too, and its last major eruption was far more recent than Kibo's, in 1707. Despite being inactive for more than 300 years, it is still classified as active by geologists.

Fuji's conical appearance is famous across the world, and is an important and sacred symbol in Japan. It is also a hugely popular tourist site. Each summer, thousands climb to its snowy peak.

Vesuvius

Vesuvius is possibly the most infamous mountain in Europe, although it is only 1,280 metres tall. It's in southern Italy, close to the city of Naples – but even closer to Pompeii.

Vesuvius became famous in a dramatic way. In 79 CE, it erupted and covered the cities of Pompeii, Herculaneum and Stabiae in lava, ash and burning mud. It wasn't until the 17th and 18th centuries that archaeologists discovered these cities buried beneath them, and began to explore their remains. Huge areas of the ancient cities were discovered, many of which were well preserved due to the speed at which they were covered. The area has provided us with an incredible insight into Roman life, and now attracts millions of visitors each year.

Vesuvius is still considered to be an active volcano – and it's thought to have erupted over 50 times during the last 2,000 years.

✏ FILL IN THE GAP

Read the sentences and choose the correct word or words to fill the gap.

They create _____ backdrops and provide extreme sports enthusiasts with climbing, trekking and skiing opportunities – but what are they, exactly?

Mountains are areas of land that are higher than the land around them, but different definitions based on _____ exist.

However, mountains can rise to _____ of metres in height.

Some of the world's best-known ranges include the _____ in Europe, the Rocky Mountains in North America and the Himalayas in Asia.

Mountains are created by areas of Earth's solid crust, called _____, moving on the liquid magma beneath them.

Some are created by magma _____ from gaps between the plates.

Others have been created by underwater _____, when lava reaches the surface.

Some of the world's best-known mountains – although not all the highest – are _____, Kilimanjaro, Fuji and Vesuvius.

Many _____ climbing enthusiasts have attempted to climb it.

Climbing Everest requires intensive _____ and can cost a lot of money.

It is located on the northern border of _____, overlooking Kenya.

It is situated to the _____ of the capital city of Tokyo.

Fuji's conical appearance is famous across the world, and is an important and sacred _____ in Japan.

Each summer, thousands climb to its _____ peak.

Vesuvius is still considered to be an _____ volcano.

 **MATCHING**

Draw a line with a ruler to match the information.

Fuji	5,895 metres
Everest	1,280 metres
Kilimanjaro	8,848 metres
Vesuvius	3,776 metres

Fuji	Italy
Vesuvius	Himalayas
Everest	Africa
Kilimanjaro	west of Tokyo

nearly 300 people died	Fuji
three inactive volcanoes	Kilimanjaro
erupted in 79 CE	Everest
major eruption in 1707	Vesuvius

requires intensive training	Vesuvius
Shira is the oldest peak	Everest
classified as active	Fuji
destroyed Pompeii	Kilimanjaro

Vesuvius	raise money for charities
Fuji	three inactive volcanoes
Kilimanjaro	conical appearance
Everest	insight into Roman life

 **LABEL**

Label the statements with the correct mountain.

8,848 m tall	
located near to Tokyo	
located close to Naples	
conical appearance	
Kibo is its youngest peak	
destroyed Stabiae	

Label the information with the correct mountain.

3,776 m tall	
found in Europe	
summit 5,895 m	
temporarily inactive	
nearly 300 deaths	
erupted 360,000 years ago	

Label the information with the correct mountain.

located on northern border of Tanzania	
found in the Himalayas	
Shira is its oldest peak	
thousands climb to this peak each year	
1,280 m tall	
erupted over 50 times in last 2,000 years	

 **TRUE OR FALSE**

Read the sentences. Put a tick in the correct box to show which sentences are *true* and which are *false*.

A group of mountains is known as a gang of mountains.   True ☐   False ☐

The Himalayas are found in Asia.   True ☐   False ☐

The Alps are found in the United States.   True ☐   False ☐

The Rocky Mountains are found in Mexico.   True ☐   False ☐

Some mountains are created by underwater volcanoes.   True ☐   False ☐

Mountains form when the Earth's crust is pushed together and up.   True ☐   False ☐

The most famous mountain is Kilimanjaro.   True ☐   False ☐

Mount Everest is in the Himalayas.   True ☐   False ☐

Mount Fuji is 8,848 metres tall.   True ☐   False ☐

Queues can form at the summit of Mount Everest.   True ☐   False ☐

3,000 climbers have conquered Mount Vesuvius.   True ☐   False ☐

Mount Everest is the highest mountain in the world.   True ☐   False ☐

Kilimanjaro's summit is almost 5,000 metres lower that Mount Everest.   True ☐   False ☐

Kilimanjaro is in Africa.   True ☐   False ☐

Nearly 300 people have died climbing Mount Everest.   True ☐   False ☐

Mount Vesuvius is located in Europe.   True ☐   False ☐

Mount Vesuvius played a significant role in history.   True ☐   False ☐

Archaeologists discovered ancient cities buried by Mount Fuji.   True ☐   False ☐

Mount Everest is an active volcano.   True ☐   False ☐

Pompeii was a Roman city.   True ☐   False ☐

◉ MULTIPLE CHOICE

Circle the correct answer for each of the following questions.

Where can mountains be found?

| in Europe | above sea level | on continents | all over the world |

What is the correct name for a group of mountains?

| a mountain gang | a mountain range | a mountain team | a mountain group |

What is the name of the best-known group of mountains in Europe?

| the Alps | the Andes | the Himalayas | the Rockies |

Which of the following creates mountains?

| floods | tectonic plates | earthquakes | avalanches |

What is the height of Mount Everest?

| 5,895 metres | 2,950 metres | 3,776 metres | 8,848 metres |

Which of the following measures 1,280 metres tall?

| Fuji | Kilimanjaro | Vesuvius | Everest |

Which modern-day city is Pompeii closest to?

| Tokyo | Tanzania | Nepal | Naples |

Mount Fuji has been inactive for…

| less than 100 years | 200 years | more than 300 years | 50 years |

Which of the following is the name of the oldest peak on Mount Kilimanjaro?

| Mawensi | Shira | Kibo | Fuji |

When did Mount Vesuvius erupt and destroy Pompeii?

| 79 CE | 97 CE | 17 CE | 73 CE |

Comprehension Ninja 9–10 © Andrew Jennings, 2020

123 SEQUENCING

Look at _Mountains of the world_. Number the statements from 1 to 5 to show the order they occur in the text. Look at the first line of each paragraph tow help you.

Undoubtedly the most famous mountain of them all, Everest is in the Himalayas in Asia.

Huge and often striking, mountains can be found all over the world.

Mountains are created by areas of the Earth's solid crust, called 'plates', moving on the liquid magma beneath them.

Vesuvius is still considered to be an active volcano – and it's thought to have erupted over 50 times during the last 2,000 years.

Fuji, the highest mountain in Japan, is 3,776 metres tall.

Look at the second to last paragraph in _Mountains of the world_. Number the statements from 1 to 5 to show the order they occur in the text.

Vesuvius became famous in a dramatic way.

In 79 CE, it erupted and covered the cities of Pompeii, Herculaneum and Stabiae in lava, ash and burning mud.

The area has provided us with an incredible insight into Roman life, and now attracts millions of visitors each year.

It wasn't until the 17th and 18th centuries that archaeologists discovered these cities buried beneath them, and began to explore their remains.

Huge areas of the ancient cities were discovered, many of which were well preserved due to the speed at which they were covered.

Look at _Mountains of the world_. Number the statements from 1 to 5 to show the order they occur in the text.

It is the highest mountain in the world, at a staggering 8,848 metres high.

Some of the world's best-known ranges include the Alps in Europe, the Rocky Mountains in North America and the Himalayas in Asia.

Over 5,000 brave climbers are said to have reached the top, but nearly 300 have died during their attempts.

Kibo is the youngest and had the most recent major eruption – but that was around 360,000 years ago.

Huge areas of the ancient cities were discovered, many of which were well preserved due to the speed at which they were covered.

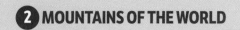

These questions are about *Mountains of the world*.

Look at paragraph one. Find and copy a word that suggests that mountains are extremely beautiful.

_____

Look at paragraph two. Find and copy a word that refers to the top of a mountain.

_____

Look at paragraph three. Find and copy a word that suggests that magma is forced out of the ground with explosive force.

_____

Look at the Everest section. Find and copy a word that suggests that lines of people can be found on Everest.

_____

Look at the Kilimanjaro section. Find and copy a word that suggests that Kenya can be seen from the top of the mountain.

_____

Look at the Fuji section. Find and copy a word that suggests that there is still a possibility that Mount Fuji could erupt.

_____

Look at the Vesuvius section. Find and copy a word that suggests Vesuvius is well known.

_____

Look at the Vesuvius section. Find and copy two words that suggest that ancient cities were maintained in a state that was near perfect because of the ash.

_____

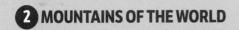UNDERLINE OR HIGHLIGHT

Read the paragraphs below and then follow the instructions.

Vesuvius is possibly the most infamous mountain in Europe, although it is only 1,280 metres tall. It's in southern Italy, close to the city of Naples – but even closer to Pompeii.

Vesuvius became famous in a dramatic way. In 79 CE, it erupted and covered the cities of Pompeii, Herculaneum and Stabiae in lava, ash and burning mud. It wasn't until the 17th and 18th centuries that archaeologists discovered these cities buried beneath them, and began to explore their remains. Huge areas of the ancient cities were discovered, many of which were well preserved due to the speed at which they were covered. The area has provided us with an incredible insight into Roman life, and now attracts millions of visitors each year.

Vesuvius is still considered to be an active volcano – and it's thought to have erupted over 50 times during the last 2,000 years.

Underline or highlight a word that means to understand a complicated situation.

Underline or highlight a word that means to be covered up with earth.

Underline or highlight a word that means known because of something bad.

Underline or highlight a word that means exciting and impressive.

Underline or highlight a word that means under something else.

Underline or highlight a word that means has erupted recently or could erupt soon.

Across Great Britain, fireworks and bonfires are lit on 5 November – they serve as a colourful reminder of a significant event in history. The name of Guy Fawkes is remembered and models called 'guys' still burn on many bonfires.

However, it was actually another man, Robert Catesby, who thought up the famous and doomed Gunpowder Plot.

The plot

The Gunpowder Plot was a plan to destroy the Houses of Parliament in London and kill the king, James I.

It was motivated by religion. Protestant and Catholic people are all followers of Christianity, but with differences of opinion about how to practise their faith. James I was a Protestant ruler, and the plotters were Catholic. They wanted to return Britain to Catholic rule.

Robert Catesby: plotter in chief

Robert Catesby was born around 1572, in Warwickshire. His parents were Catholics and, after a rebellious youth, Catesby too became strongly religious.

The Gunpowder Plot was not his first attempt at rebellion. In 1601, he was involved in the failed uprising of the Earl of Essex against Queen Elizabeth's chief advisor, Robert Cecil. Catesby's actions saw him wounded, imprisoned and fined. He was also believed to have discussed a further rebellion with the Spanish government.

Catesby fell under the suspicion of the British government, who saw him as a threat.

Catesby meets Fawkes

Guy Fawkes, also known as Guido Fawkes, was born in 1570, in York. Despite coming from a Protestant background, he converted to Catholicism as a child.

When he was 21, Fawkes left England to join the Catholic Spanish army during the Eighty Years' War. He was approached to take part in the Gunpowder Plot because of his military background and experience.

The murderous plan

Catesby grew more and more dissatisfied with Protestant rule, which treated Catholics badly. His solution was the murder of the king.

He shared his plan initially with Christopher and John Wright and Thomas Winter. Winter travelled to Spain, which was under Catholic rule, hoping to find support. There he met Guy Fawkes, who returned with him. In 1604, Catesby made the plot with the Wrights, Fawkes and Thomas Percy before recruiting others to join them.

Set-up and downfall

The plotters rented a cellar below Parliament. Here, Fawkes planted barrels of gunpowder and camouflaged them with coal and firewood. He was to light the fuse and then flee to Europe. The plan seemed sure to succeed.

Then one of Catesby's recruits sent a letter to his brother-in-law Lord Monteagle, warning him to stay away from Parliament. Uncertain of its meaning, Monteagle passed on the letter, and it reached the king's advisors. Guards searched Parliament and raided the plotters' cellar – where they discovered Fawkes and the gunpowder. Fawkes was arrested and taken to the king on 5 November 1605.

The plotters' discovery

Fawkes was tortured, revealing the names of his accomplices. He was tried for his crimes and sentenced to death.

Catesby and others fled London but were tracked to Staffordshire. The authorities wanted to return them to London for a public execution. The plotters, however, decided to die fighting. After his death, Catesby's head was cut off and taken back to London.

Remember, remember …

A popular rhyme reminds people of the events of 1605:

Remember, remember, the fifth of November: gunpowder, treason and plot.

I see no reason why gunpowder treason should ever be forgot!

Bonfire Night's fireworks represent an explosion that never happened. The burning of the guy represents the plotters' punishment – but it's only Fawkes whose figure is used. Is that fair?

Perhaps, if you celebrate, you could remember Catesby instead!

✎ FILL IN THE GAP

Read the sentences and choose the correct word or words to fill the gap.

Across Great Britain, _____ are lit on 5 November.

The Gunpowder Plot was a plan to destroy the Houses of _____ in London and kill the king, James I.

However, it was actually another man, Robert Catesby, who thought up the famous and _____ Gunpowder Plot.

_____ was born around 1572, in Warwickshire.

His parents were Catholics and, after a _____ youth, Catesby too became strongly religious.

In 1601, he was involved in the failed uprising of the _____ against Queen Elizabeth's chief advisor, Robert Cecil.

Catesby fell under the _____ of the British government, who saw him as a threat.

Guy Fawkes, also known as _____, was born in 1570, in York.

When he was _____, Fawkes left England to join the Catholic Spanish army.

He was approached to take part in the Gunpowder Plot because of his _____ background and experience.

Catesby grew more and more dissatisfied with _____ rule, which treated Catholics badly.

Here, Fawkes planted barrels of gunpowder and _____ them with coal and firewood.

Guards searched Parliament and raided the _____ cellar – where they discovered Fawkes and the gunpowder.

Fawkes was _____, revealing the names of his accomplices.

After his death, Catesby's head was cut off and taken back to _____.

 Comprehension Ninja 9–10 © Andrew Jennings, 2020

 MATCHING

Draw a line with a ruler to match the information.

Robert Catesby	born 1570
Warwickshire	Guy Fawkes
York	Robert Catesby
Guy Fawkes	born around 1572

Robert Catesby	religion
plot to kill	Catholic parents
Guy Fawkes	King James I
motivated by	Protestant background

barrels	strongly religious
Guy Fawkes	Guy Fawkes
Robert Catesby	camouflaged with coal and firewood
Guido Fawkes	left England aged 21

first rebellion	suspicion of British government
Catesby dissatisfied with	failed uprising of the Earl of Essex
arrested by guards	Guy Fawkes
Robert Catesby	Protestant rule

letter	tortured
Guy Fawkes	Lord Monteagle
Protestant rule	head cut off
Robert Catesby	treated Catholics badly

 LABEL

Label the information with the correct person or place.

duo planned to blow up	
born in Warwickshire	
failed rebellion against	
thought up the gunpowder plot	
first rebellion leader	
Robert Cecil was advisor to	

Label the information with the correct person or place.

alternative name for Guy Fawkes	
Gunpowder Plot designed to kill	
Catesby shared initial plans with	
letter sent to	
Catesby fled from	
Catesby tracked to	

Label the information with the correct person or place.

born in York	
Catesby's head taken to	
fireworks and bonfires are lit	
decided to die fighting	
discovered under the Houses of Parliament	
joined the Catholic Spanish army	

 TRUE OR FALSE

Read the sentences. Put a tick in the correct box to show which sentences are *true* and which are *false*.

Fireworks and bonfires are lit on 5 November.　　True ☐　False ☐

Guy Fawkes thought up the Gunpowder Plot.　　True ☐　False ☐

The Gunpowder Plot was a plan to destroy Buckingham Palace.　　True ☐　False ☐

The Gunpowder Plot happened in 1605.　　True ☐　False ☐

Robert Cecil was Robert Catesby's advisor.　　True ☐　False ☐

Robert Catesby was born in York.　　True ☐　False ☐

Robert Catesby was involved in a failed uprising in 1601.　　True ☐　False ☐

Robert Catesby was wounded and imprisoned because of his 1601 rebellion.　　True ☐　False ☐

Robert Catesby was strongly religious.　　True ☐　False ☐

Robert Catesby fought in the Eighty Years' War.　　True ☐　False ☐

Guy Fawkes was also known as Guido Fawkes.　　True ☐　False ☐

Guy Fawkes was born in Warwickshire.　　True ☐　False ☐

Guy Fawkes joined the Spanish army aged 21.　　True ☐　False ☐

Guy Fawkes fought in the Eighty Years' War.　　True ☐　False ☐

Guy Fawkes was an advisor to Queen Elizabeth.　　True ☐　False ☐

◎ MULTIPLE CHOICE

Circle the correct answer for each of the following questions.

On which date are fireworks and bonfires lit in the UK?

| 4 November | 5 November | 6 November | 7 November |

Who was born around 1572?

| Robert Catesby | Guido Fawkes | Robert Cecil | Thomas Winter |

Who fought in the Eighty Years' War?

| Robert Catesby | Guido Fawkes | Robert Cecil | Thomas Winter |

Who were the British government suspicious of?

| Robert Catesby | Guido Fawkes | Robert Cecil | Thomas Winter |

When did Thomas Percy learn about the Gunpowder Plot?

| 1570 | 1601 | 1604 | 1605 |

Which famous building did the Gunpowder Plot aim to destroy?

| Buckingham Palace | St Paul's Cathedral | House of Commons | Houses of Parliament |

Which person did the Gunpowder Plot aim to kill?

| King James I | Queen Elizabeth | Robert Cecil | Thomas Percy |

Where was Robert Catesby's head placed?

| London | Staffordshire | Spain | York |

Where did Catesby and others hide after the plot was discovered?

| London | Staffordshire | Spain | York |

What sentence did Guy Fawkes receive when he was caught?

| death | 80 years in prison | no sentence | torture |

123 SEQUENCING

Look at *The Gunpowder Plot*. Number the statements from 1 to 5 to show the order they occur in the text. Look at the first line of each paragraph to help you.

The Gunpowder Plot was a plan to destroy the Houses of Parliament in London and kill the king, James I.

Guy Fawkes, also known as Guido Fawkes, was born in 1570, in York.

Fawkes was tortured, revealing the names of his accomplices.

Catesby grew more and more dissatisfied with Protestant rule, which treated Catholics badly.

Across Great Britain, fireworks and bonfires are lit on 5 November – they serve as a colourful reminder of a significant event in history.

Look at the 'Set up and downfall' section in *The Gunpowder Plot*. Number the statements from 1 to 5 to show the order they occur in the text.

The plotters rented a cellar below Parliament.

Uncertain of its meaning, Monteagle passed on the letter, and it reached the king's advisors.

He was to light the fuse and then flee to Europe.

Then one of Catesby's recruits sent a letter to his brother-in-law Lord Monteagle, warning him to stay away from Parliament.

Here, Fawkes planted barrels of gunpowder and camouflaged them with coal and firewood.

Look at *The Gunpowder Plot*. Number the statements from 1 to 5 to show the order they occur in the text.

He was also believed to have discussed a further rebellion with the Spanish government.

In 1604, Catesby established the plot with the Wrights, Fawkes and Thomas Percy before recruiting others to join them.

Guards searched Parliament and raided the plotters' cellar – where they discovered Fawkes and the gunpowder.

They wanted to return Britain to Catholic rule.

When he was 21, Fawkes left England to join the Catholic Spanish army during the Eighty Years' War.

FIND AND COPY

These questions are about *The Gunpowder Plot*.

Look at paragraph one. Find and copy a word that suggests that the 5 November is an important historical event.

_____

Look at the paragraph beginning 'However…'. Find and copy a word that suggests that the Gunpowder Plot was going to fail.

_____

Look at the 'The plot' section. Find and copy a word that suggests that religion was the main reason for the plot happening.

_____

Look at the 'The plot' section. Find and copy a word that suggests that people didn't have the same opinion.

_____

Look at the 'Robert Catesby: plotter in chief' section. Find and copy a word that suggests that Catesby didn't follow the rules when he was younger.

_____

Look at the paragraph beginning 'The Gunpowder Plot…'. Find and copy a word that suggests that the uprising of the Earl of Essex did not work.

_____

Look at the 'Catesby meets Fawkes' section. Find and copy a word that suggests that Fawkes changed his religion.

_____

Look at the 'Murderous plan' section. Find and copy a word that suggests that Catesby was unhappy with the rulers.

_____

✎ UNDERLINE OR HIGHLIGHT

Read the paragraphs below and then follow the instructions.

The plotters' discovery

Fawkes was tortured, revealing the names of his accomplices. He was tried for his crimes and sentenced to death.

Catesby and others fled London but were tracked to Staffordshire. The authorities wanted to return them to London for a public execution. The plotters, however, decided to die fighting. After his death, Catesby's head was cut off and taken back to London.

Remember, remember …

A popular rhyme reminds people of the events of 1605:

Remember, remember, the fifth of November: gunpowder, treason and plot.

I see no reason why gunpowder treason should ever be forgot!

Bonfire Night's fireworks represent an explosion that never happened. The burning of the guy represents the plotters' punishment – but it's only Fawkes whose figure is used. Is that fair?

Underline or highlight a word that means a crime which hopes to overthrow the government.

Underline or highlight a word that means in front of all the people in a community.

Underline or highlight a word that means to deliberately cause pain over a period of time.

Underline or highlight a word that means someone who helps commit a crime.

Underline or highlight a word that means an explosive substance.

Underline or highlight a word that means to kill as a punishment for a crime.

4 QUEEN VICTORIA

You may know about the Victorians, but how much do you know about Queen Victoria herself? As a baby, she had been only fifth in line to the throne. However, she reigned over the United Kingdom for more than 60 years.

Victoria's early life

Victoria was born at Kensington Palace, in London, on 24 May 1819. She was the daughter of Prince Edward and Victoria Mary Louisa, also known as the Duke and Duchess of Kent.

As a young royal, Victoria had strict rules imposed on her by her protective mother. She was made to sleep in her mother's room and was not allowed to play with other children. Her 132 dolls did little to help her loneliness, and her closest childhood companion was her dog, Dash.

Victoria enjoyed spending time painting and drawing as she became older, and also kept a diary. She wrote lengthy entries in diaries throughout her life, and many still exist today. They give historians great insight into her character.

Becoming queen

When she was born, it seemed unlikely that Victoria would become queen. Victoria lost her father and two of her uncles before she was 12, though, meaning she was next in line to the throne.

Victoria's third uncle, King William IV, died in 1837, when she was just 18. Her lavish coronation took place just over a week later at Westminster Abbey, in London. She became the first monarch to live at Buckingham Palace.

Starting a family

Victoria proposed to her German cousin Prince Albert in 1839, and they were married the next year. The cousins had been close since Albert's first visit when Victoria was 17, and their marriage was, by all accounts, extremely happy. The couple had nine children.

Due to the Queen's responsibilities, Albert was said to have been very involved in the children's upbringing. Victoria was extremely attached to her children, though, and set the example of considering them the heart of a family – which was an unusual position, at the time.

Comprehension Ninja 9–10 © Andrew Jennings, 2020

Victorian England

During Victoria's reign, Britain experienced huge expansion in trade, mechanical production, railways, bridges, underground sewers and power distribution networks. As a consequence, cities such as Manchester, Leeds and Birmingham grew significantly. Major advances in science were made, such as Darwin's theory of evolution. Telephones, cameras and electric lights were invented. Victoria's focus on family and Albert's German traditions also established Christmas as we know it today.

The British Empire also expanded, to include places such as Canada, Australia and India. The Empire's colonies often treated the local population extremely badly, but Queen Victoria was rarely involved personally in the business of other nations.

The marriages of Victoria's children, and Victoria's ability to speak many languages, meant that she developed connections to many other royal families in Europe. She became related by marriage to so many of them that she was sometimes known as 'the Grandmother of Europe'.

The final Christmas

Victoria's health and spirits declined after Albert's death in 1861, which happened when she was only 42. However, she kept up her public duties until her death.

As was her tradition, she spent the Christmas of 1900 at Osborne House on the Isle of Wight. Her health, however, quickly deteriorated, and she was unable to return to London. On 22 January 1901, at the age of 81, Queen Victoria died – with her son, the future King Edward VII, by her side.

Queen Victoria's legacy lives on throughout the world, and not only through the progress her era saw. Her name is also remembered in the hundreds (perhaps thousands) of streets, squares and pubs named after her. Do you know one?

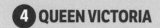

FILL IN THE GAP

Read the sentences and choose the correct word or words to fill the gap.

As a baby, she had been only fifth in line to the _____.

However, she _____ over the United Kingdom for more than 60 years.

Victoria was born at _____, in London, on 24 May 1819.

She was the daughter of Prince Edward and Victoria Mary Louisa, also known as the Duke and Duchess of _____.

As a young royal, Victoria had strict rules imposed on her by her _____ mother.

She was made to sleep in her mother's room and was not allowed to _____ with other children.

Her _____ dolls did little to help her loneliness, and her closest childhood companion was her dog, Dash.

Victoria enjoyed spending time painting and drawing as she became older, and also kept a _____.

They give historians great insight into her _____.

Victoria's third uncle, _____, died in 1837, when she was just 18.

Her lavish coronation took place just over a week later at _____, in London.

She became the first monarch to live at _____.

Victoria's health and spirits _____ after Albert's death in 1861, which happened when she was only 42.

The couple had _____ children.

Telephones, cameras and electric lights were _____.

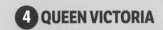 
Draw a line with a ruler to match the information.

Queen Victoria's birthplace	May 1819
reigned for	January 1901
Victoria born	Kensington Palace
Queen Victoria died	over 60 years

mother	Dash
dog	Prince Edward
father	Duke and Duchess of Kent
mother and father known as	Victoria Mary Louisa

mother	painting
dolls	diary
enjoyed	strict rules
kept a	132

known as	fifth in line for throne
as a baby	Osborne House
Buckingham Palace	the Grandmother of Europe
spent Christmas at	first monarch

Queen Victoria's son	1861
Queen Victoria's age when Prince Albert died	nine
Prince Albert died	42
number of children	King Edward VII

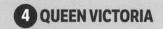

LABEL

Label the information with the correct date or number.

Queen Victoria reigned for	
Queen Victoria born	
number of dolls	
became Queen	
married Prince Albert	
became Queen aged	

Label the information with the correct date or number.

Prince Albert died	
Queen Victoria's age when Albert died	
number of children	
Queen Victoria's age when she met Albert	
Queen Victoria died	
Queen Victoria's age when she died	

Label the information with the place name.

spent Christmas of 1900	
locations in the British Empire	
lavish coronation took place	
first monarch to live in	
Queen Victoria born in	
Victoria's parents were Duke and Duchess of	

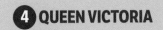 

TRUE OR FALSE

Read the sentences. Put a tick in the correct box to show which sentences are *true* and which are *false*.

Queen Victoria reigned for over 70 years.   True ☐   False ☐

Victoria was born on 23 May 1819.   True ☐   False ☐

She was the daughter of King William.   True ☐   False ☐

Victoria was born at Buckingham Palace.   True ☐   False ☐

Her parents were the Duke and Duchess of Kensington.   True ☐   False ☐

Her mother was a very relaxed parent.   True ☐   False ☐

Victoria was not allowed to sleep in her own room.   True ☐   False ☐

Victoria had 213 dolls.   True ☐   False ☐

Victoria shared a bedroom with her mother.   True ☐   False ☐

Victoria enjoyed writing in a diary.   True ☐   False ☐

Many of queen Victoria's diaries still exist.   True ☐   False ☐

As a baby, Victoria was sixth in line for the throne.   True ☐   False ☐

Victoria became queen following the death of King William IV.   True ☐   False ☐

Her coronation took place in Westminster Abbey.   True ☐   False ☐

Victoria was crowned as Queen on her 21st birthday.   True ☐   False ☐

Victoria was married to her cousin.   True ☐   False ☐

Albert proposed to Victoria.   True ☐   False ☐

Queen Victoria had nine children.   True ☐   False ☐

Albert was very involved in the children's upbringing.   True ☐   False ☐

Queen Victoria died in 1901.   True ☐   False ☐

◎ MULTIPLE CHOICE

Circle the correct answer for each of the following questions.

For how many years did Queen Victoria reign?

| 50 years | over 70 years | over 60 years | less than 20 years |

How old was Queen Victoria when she died?

| 79 | 80 | 81 | 82 |

How many children did Queen Victoria have?

| one | three | six | nine |

Queen Victoria married her…

| best friend | brother | uncle | cousin |

Victoria became queen after the death of…

| Prince Albert | Queen Elizabeth | King William IV | King Arthur |

What was Queen Victoria sometimes known as?

| Europe's sister | Mother of Europe | Queen of Europe | Grandmother of Europe |

Which cities grew under her rule?

| Manchester, Birmingham and Leeds | Birmingham, Leeds and Liverpool | Leeds, London and Stoke | Manchester, York and Leeds |

Who was king after Queen Victoria died?

| Queen Elizabeth II | King William IV | King Edward VII | Prince Albert |

In which year did Prince Albert die?

| 1871 | 1861 | 1961 | 1837 |

Where did Queen Victoria spend Christmas in the month of her death?

| Manchester | Buckingham Palace | Kensington Palace | Osborne House |

123 SEQUENCING

Look at _Queen Victoria_. Number the statements from 1 to 5 to show the order they occur in the text. Look at the first line of each paragraph to help you.

Victoria enjoyed spending time painting and drawing as she became older, and also kept a diary.

As a young royal, Victoria had strict rules imposed on her by her protective mother.

Victoria proposed to her German cousin Prince Albert in 1839, and they were married the next year.

Victoria's health and spirits declined after Albert's death in 1861, which happened when she was only 42.

Victoria was born at Kensington Palace, in London, on 24 May 1819.

Look at the section titled 'The final Christmas' in _Queen Victoria_. Number the statements from 1 to 5 to show the order they occur in the text.

Queen Victoria's legacy lives on throughout the world, and not only through the progress her era saw.

As was her tradition, she spent the Christmas of 1900 at Osborne House on the Isle of Wight.

Her health, however, quickly deteriorated, and she was unable to return to London.

On 22 January 1901, at the age of 81, Queen Victoria died – with her son, the future King Edward VII, by her side.

Victoria's health and spirits declined after Albert's death in 1861, which happened when she was only 42.

Look at _Queen Victoria_. Number the statements from 1 to 5 to show the order they occur in the text.

She was the daughter of Prince Edward and Victoria Mary Louisa, also known as the Duke and Duchess of Kent.

Her 132 dolls did little to help her loneliness, and her closest childhood companion was her dog, Dash.

The cousins had been close since Albert's first visit when Victoria was 17, and their marriage was, by all accounts, extremely happy.

She became the first monarch to live at Buckingham Palace.

She became related by marriage to so many of them that she was sometimes known as 'the Grandmother of Europe'.

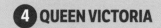 FIND AND COPY

These questions are about *Queen Victoria*.

Look at paragraph one. Find and copy a word that suggests that Queen Victoria ruled the United Kingdom.

_____

Look at the 'Victoria's early life' section. Find and copy a word that suggests that Victoria had clear and firm rules when she was a child.

_____

Look at the 'Victoria's early life' section. Find and copy a word that suggests that Victoria had few or no friends and spent lots of her time alone during her childhood.

_____

Look at the 'Victoria's early life' section. Find and copy a word that suggests that Victoria's diary entries were long and detailed.

_____

Look at the paragraph beginning 'When she was born…'. Find and copy a word that suggests it wasn't expected that Victoria would become queen.

_____

Look at the paragraph beginning 'Victoria's third uncle…'. Find and copy a word that suggests that her coronation was extravagant and cost a lot of money.

_____

Look at the 'Starting a family' section. Find and copy a word suggests Victoria asked Prince Albert to marry her.

_____

Look at the 'The final Christmas' section. Find and copy a word suggests that Victoria's health became worse.

_____

   Comprehension Ninja 9–10 © Andrew Jennings, 2020

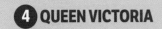

✎ UNDERLINE OR HIGHLIGHT

Read the paragraphs below and then follow the instructions.

During Victoria's reign, Britain experienced huge expansion in trade, mechanical production, railways, bridges, underground sewers and power distribution networks. As a consequence, cities such as Manchester, Leeds and Birmingham grew significantly. Major advances in science were made, such as Darwin's theory of evolution. Telephones, cameras and electric lights were invented. Victoria's focus on family and Albert's German traditions also established Christmas as we know it today.

The British Empire also expanded, to include places such as Canada, Australia and India. The Empire's colonies often treated the local population extremely badly, but Queen Victoria was rarely involved personally in the business of other nations.

The marriages of Victoria's children, and Victoria's ability to speak many languages, meant that she developed connections to many other royal families in Europe. She became related by marriage to so many of them that she was sometimes known as 'the Grandmother of Europe'.

Underline or highlight a word that means to become greater or larger in size.

Underline or highlight a word that means does not happen very often.

Underline or highlight a word that means to deliver to a number of different places.

Underline or highlight a word that means countries controlled by more powerful countries.

Underline or highlight a word that means belong to the same family.

5 THE CIRCULATORY SYSTEM

The circulatory system (also known as the cardiovascular system) is the complex network that transports blood in a cycle through the body. The blood supplies water, oxygen and nutrients to all the body's tissues and organs. It also takes away their waste: carbon dioxide and dead cells. The circulatory system is made up of three main parts: the heart, blood vessels and blood.

The heart

The heart pumps blood all around the circulatory system. It's a muscle that repeatedly squeezes, or 'contracts', and relaxes. We can hear its contractions as heartbeats.

The heart consists of four chambers – two on the left and two on the right. The two upper chambers are called the atria, while the lower chambers are known as the ventricles.

When the heart contracts, it pushes blood out, into blood vessels. First, it is pumped out from the right side of the heart, and is taken to the lungs. There, it collects oxygen from air that has been breathed in, and deposits carbon dioxide that will be breathed out. After this, the oxygen-carrying blood travels back to the left side of the heart, ready to be pumped to other parts of the body.

Blood vessels

Blood vessels form a network of small tubes that provide blood with routes to every organ and tissue in the body.

Arteries carry blood containing oxygen and other nutrients from the heart. They branch away from each other, decreasing in size as they approach each body part. The oxygen and nutrients travel with this body part and are replaced by carbon dioxide and other waste.

Capillaries connect the smallest arteries to the smallest veins. Veins transport the blood carrying the body's waste back towards the heart, joining together and increasing in size as they get nearer to it.

Comprehension Ninja 9–10 © Andrew Jennings, 2020

Blood

An average person has around five litres of blood inside their body. It travels astonishingly quickly: it takes only around 20 seconds for one red blood cell to be transported around the entirety of a human body.

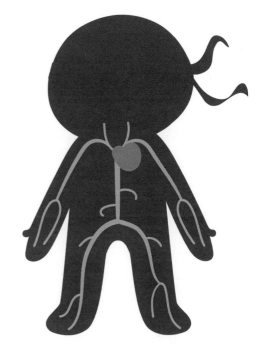

Blood consists of four main parts: red blood cells, white blood cells, plasma and platelets. Red blood cells carry oxygen and carbon dioxide around the body. White blood cells attack the unknown cells of infections and diseases and consume much of the waste the blood collects. Plasma transports nutrients, hormones and proteins around the body, which can also fight infections. Platelets help to stop bleeding from cuts by sticking to the broken blood vessels and each other. This forms clots that can plug the cut.

Although all blood has these four components with the same purposes, not everyone's blood is the same. Blood is divided into four main blood groups that contain different disease-fighting proteins in their plasma. The blood groups have been labelled 'A', 'B', 'AB' and 'O'. Blood type O is the most common. In the United Kingdom, nearly half of the population has blood type O.

Injured people who have lost a lot of blood sometimes need to receive blood from another person. If this happens, it is vital that the right type of blood is given to them. If the wrong blood type is used, white blood cells and proteins from the injured person may mistake the cells in the new blood for disease and attack them.

For this reason, it's vital that people of all blood groups donate blood. In the United Kingdom, the youngest age you can donate is 17. You can always encourage others to donate, though!

 FILL IN THE GAP

Read the sentences and choose the correct word or words to fill the gap.

The circulatory system (also known as the cardiovascular system) is the _____ that transports blood in a cycle through the body.

The _____ system is made up of three main parts: the heart, blood vessels and blood.

It also takes away their waste: _____ and dead cells.

The _____ pumps blood all around the circulatory system.

The heart consists of _____ chambers.

The two upper chambers are called the _____, while the lower chambers are known as the ventricles.

When the heart _____, it pushes blood out, into blood vessels.

_____ connect the smallest arteries to the smallest veins.

Blood vessels form a network of small tubes that provide blood with _____ to every organ and tissue in the body.

An average person has around _____ of blood inside their body.

Arteries carry blood containing _____ and other nutrients from the heart.

Veins transport the blood carrying the body's _____ back towards the heart, joining together and increasing in size as they get nearer to it.

It travels astonishingly quickly: it takes only around _____ for one red blood cell to be transported around the entirety of a human body.

In the _____, nearly half of the population has blood type O.

For this reason, it's vital that people of all blood groups _____ blood.

 **MATCHING**

Draw a line with a ruler to match the information.

the heart	small tubes
the blood vessels	three main parts
blood volume	five litres
circulatory system	muscle

contracts	four chambers
the blood	blood containing oxygen
arteries	white blood cells
the heart	squeezes

veins	atria and ventricles
capillaries	platelets and plasma
the heart	blood containing carbon dioxide
the blood	connectors

plasma transports	17
blood types	atria
age to donate blood in the UK	proteins
upper chambers	A, B, AB and O

platelets	ventricles
most common blood group	cause clotting
plasma	O
lower chambers	transports nutrients

 LABEL

Label the description with the correct body part.

a complex network of organs and vessels	
a muscle	
has three main parts	
travels around the body in 20 seconds	
stops bleeding	
cell type that fights infections	

Label the description with the correct body part.

around five litres in the body	
carry blood containing oxygen	
transports nutrients and hormones	
lower chambers of the heart	
connects smallest arteries to smallest veins	
blood pumping muscle around the circulatory system	

Label the description with the correct information.

transported inside blood vessels	
has four chambers	
transport the blood carrying waste	
blood groups	
age from which you can donate blood	
upper chambers of the heart	

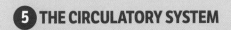 

 TRUE OR FALSE

Read the sentences. Put a tick in the correct box to show which sentences are *true* and which are *false*.

The circulatory system only involves the heart.	True ☐	False ☐
The circulatory system is also known as the cardiovascular system.	True ☐	False ☐
The circulatory system involves four main parts.	True ☐	False ☐
Blood type A is the most common blood type.	True ☐	False ☐
Plasma transports nutrients and hormones.	True ☐	False ☐
Platelets help blood to clot.	True ☐	False ☐
The heart is made up of five different layers.	True ☐	False ☐
The heart consists of four chambers.	True ☐	False ☐
The heart's lower chambers are called ventricles.	True ☐	False ☐
The heart's upper chambers are called vessels.	True ☐	False ☐
The blood is pumped from the heart to the lungs to collect oxygen.	True ☐	False ☐
Blood is transported around the body inside blood vessels.	True ☐	False ☐
Arteries carry blood containing oxygen.	True ☐	False ☐
Veins transport blood back towards the heart.	True ☐	False ☐
Capillaries connect the smallest arteries to the veins.	True ☐	False ☐

◎ MULTIPLE CHOICE

Circle the correct answer for each of the following questions.

Which of the following transports nutrients, hormones and proteins around the body?

| white blood cells | blood | plasma | vessels |

What are the four main blood groups?

| A, B, BA and O | A, B, AB and O | A, E, D and O | A, B, D and C |

What is the most common blood group?

| O | AB | A | B |

Which of the following helps stop bleeding and forms clots?

| white blood cells | antigens | plasma | platelets |

Which of the following carries oxygen around the body?

| white blood cells | red blood cells | plasma | vessels |

Which of the following fights infections in the body?

| white blood cells | the heart | plasma | platelets |

How much blood does the average person have in their body?

| four litres | five litres | six litres | seven litres |

Which of the following transports the body's waste back to the heart?

| heart | arteries | veins | capillaries |

Which of the following transports oxygen and nutrients from the heart?

| lungs | capillaries | veins | arteries |

Where does the blood collect oxygen from?

| heart | brain | arteries | lungs |

123 SEQUENCING

Look at *The circulatory system*. Number the statements from 1 to 5 to show the order they occur in the text. Look at the first line of each paragraph to help you.

When the heart contracts, it pushes blood out, into blood vessels. ☐

The circulatory system (also known as the cardiovascular system) is the complex network that transports blood in a cycle through the body. ☐

The heart pumps blood all around the circulatory system. ☐

Injured people who have lost a lot of blood sometimes need to receive blood from another person. ☐

Blood consists of four main parts: red blood cells, white blood cells, plasma and platelets. ☐

Look at the 'Blood' section in *The circulatory system*. Number the statements from 1 to 5 to show the order they occur in the text.

Blood consists of four main parts: red blood cells, white blood cells, plasma and platelets. ☐

Plasma transports nutrients, hormones and proteins around the body, which can also fight infections. ☐

Red blood cells carry oxygen and carbon dioxide around the body. ☐

It travels astonishingly quickly: it takes only around 20 seconds for one red blood cell to be transported around the entirety of a human body. ☐

An average person has around five litres of blood inside their body. ☐

Look at *The circulatory system*. Number the statements from 1 to 5 to show the order they occur in the text.

After this, the oxygen-carrying blood travels back to the left side of the heart, ready to be pumped to other parts of the body. ☐

If the wrong blood type is used, white blood cells and proteins from the injured person may mistake the cells in the new blood for disease and attack them. ☐

Capillaries connect the smallest arteries to the smallest veins. ☐

Blood is divided into four main blood groups that contain different disease-fighting proteins in their plasma. ☐

Plasma transports nutrients, hormones and proteins around the body, which can also fight infections. ☐

 FIND AND COPY

These questions are about *The circulatory system*.

Look at paragraph one. Find and copy a word that suggests that the circulatory system starts and finishes in the same place.

_____

Look at the 'The heart' section. Find and copy a word that suggests that the heart beats over and over again without stopping.

_____

Look at the 'The heart' section. Find and copy a word that suggests that when it pushes blood out, the heart squeezes.

_____

Look at the 'The heart' section. Find and copy a word that suggests that the blood gathers and takes oxygen from the lungs.

_____

Look at the 'Blood vessels' section. Find a copy a word that suggest that blood vessels are like a web of tubes.

_____

Look at the paragraph beginning 'Blood consists of…'. Find and copy a word that suggests battles take place in the body.

_____

Look at the paragraph beginning 'Injured people who…'. Find and copy a word that suggests that giving injured people the correct type of blood is important.

_____

Look at the paragraph beginning 'For this reason…'. Find and copy a word that suggests that some people give their own blood to help others, for free.

_____

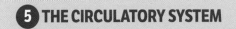 

UNDERLINE OR HIGHLIGHT

Read the paragraphs below and then follow the instructions.

An average person has around five litres of blood inside their body. It travels astonishingly quickly: it takes only around 20 seconds for one red blood cell to be transported around the entirety of a human body.

Blood consists of four main parts: red blood cells, white blood cells, plasma and platelets. Red blood cells carry oxygen and carbon dioxide around the body. White blood cells attack the unknown cells of infections and diseases and consume much of the waste the blood collects. Plasma transports nutrients, hormones and proteins around the body, which can also fight infections. Platelets help to stop bleeding from cuts by sticking to the broken blood vessels and each other. This forms clots that can plug the cut.

Although all blood has these four components with the same purposes, not everyone's blood is the same. Blood is divided into four main blood groups that contain different disease-fighting proteins in their plasma. The blood groups have been labelled 'A', 'B', 'AB' and 'O'. Blood type O is the most common. In the United Kingdom, nearly half of the population has blood type O.

Underline or highlight a word that means something is moved from one place to another.

Underline or highlight a word that means something is surprising.

Underline or highlight a word that means to be made up of particular parts.

Underline or highlight a word that means is found in large numbers.

Underline or highlight a word that means a disease caused by germs or bacteria.

6 ORDNANCE SURVEY MAPS

Ordnance Survey maps are extremely detailed. They contain information about the changing landscape and points of interest, such as roads, forests, buildings, rivers – even car parks! Ordnance Survey is an official mapping company for Great Britain, and is owned by the government.

Why were Ordnance Survey maps first made?

The company name, 'Ordnance Survey', hints at how it began. 'Ordnance' means military supplies, and a 'survey' is a study of how different points on land relate to each other. The first Ordnance Survey maps were created following a rebellion in 1745, when the military realised it didn't have a detailed enough understanding of the land in Scotland for planning battles and moving troops. Later, when the French Revolution was happening, the defence ministry – the Board of Ordnance – was asked to survey the south of England in case of attack from France.

Who began the mapping?

William Roy, a 21-year-old engineer, was asked to conduct the military survey of Scotland. His 'Great Map' included details of natural and man-made features such as hills, rivers, types of land, roads and buildings. It took him eight years to complete. Roy's teams included around eight people, who used compasses to measure angles, long chains to measure distances and completed drawings of what they saw.

The Ordnance Survey in war

The Ordnance Survey played a significant role in Britain's World War I and World War II campaigns. The company was no longer a small team of men with chains, but over 800 trained topographers (map-planners), observers, draughtsmen and printers. These people worked tirelessly from 1915 onwards, not only mapping the country but also plotting the positions of trenches, machine-guns and batteries belonging to the allies and the enemy.

By 1915, Ordnance Survey was producing 90 per cent of all war maps in Britain. By the end of the war they had supplied almost 20 million maps, plans and diagrams to the military, providing a vital tool for the war effort. However, their primary role was actually to work on the front line of battle, to assess the distance of enemy artillery targets accurately. It was a dangerous job, and 67 members of the Ordnance Survey team lost their lives during World War I.

Modern Ordnance Survey maps

Nowadays, it may seem usual for a map to show hills, roads and water bodies. Ordnance Survey maps continue to be innovative, though, and offer much more.

Like any piece of paper, maps are flat, but the land they cover is often quite hilly. Contour lines are a way of showing on a map how high the land is. They join together points of equal height and never cross. When contour lines appear close together, this means the land slopes sharply and would be steep to climb. The further apart the contour lines are, the flatter the land will be.

The maps often also use symbols instead of words to label features and make the maps clearer: as there are so many features, there wouldn't be enough space to note everything in words. The symbols could be small pictures, letters, lines or coloured areas, and they show features such as campsites, youth hostels, historic sites and bus stations. Fortunately, there will usually be a key next to the map to tell you what they mean.

Ordnance Survey maps are still used by the military, but now they are also vital for people who are planning buildings, hiking, orienteering or even simply finding country pubs. If you have a chance to look at a map of your region, try studying its tiny details for yourself. You should be able to spot exactly where you are.

✏ FILL IN THE GAP

Read the sentences and choose the correct word or words to fill the gap.

'Ordnance' means _____, and a 'survey' is a study of how different points on land relate to each other.

The first Ordnance Survey maps were created following a _____ in 1745, when the military realised it didn't have a detailed enough understanding of the land in Scotland for planning battles and moving troops.

Later, when the _____ was happening, the defence ministry – the Board of Ordnance – was asked to survey the south of England in case of attack from France.

Ordnance Survey maps are extremely _____.

_____, a 21-year-old engineer, was asked to conduct the military survey of Scotland.

His 'Great Map' included details of natural and _____ features such as hills, rivers, types of land, roads and buildings.

It took him _____ years to complete.

The company was no longer a small team of men with chains, but over 800 trained _____ (map-planners), observers, draughtsmen and printers.

These people worked tirelessly from 1915 onwards, not only mapping the country but also plotting the positions of _____, machine-guns and batteries belonging to the allies and the enemy.

By the end of the war they had supplied almost _____ maps, plans and diagrams to the military, providing a vital tool for the war effort.

However, their primary role was actually to work on the front line of battle, to assess the distance of enemy _____ targets accurately.

Contour lines are a way of showing on a map how _____ the land is.

When contour lines appear close together, this means the land _____ sharply and would be steep to climb.

The maps often also use _____ instead of words to label features and make the maps clearer: as there are so many features, there wouldn't be enough space to note everything in words.

The symbols could be small pictures, letters, lines or coloured areas, and they show features such as _____, youth hostels, historic sites and bus stations.

Draw a line with a ruler to match the information.

Ordnance Survey	information about car parks
rebellion	extremely detailed
Ordnance Survey maps	1745
maps record	owned by the government

William Roy	eight years to complete
distance measured using	21 years old
survey of Scotland	eight people
Roy's team	chains

mapped during war	20 million maps
significant role in	trenches and batteries
90 per cent of war maps in Britain	Ordnance Survey produced
Ordnance Survey supplied	World War I and II campaigns

extremely detailed maps of	67 members of Ordnance Survey
primary role	roads, forests, parks and rivers
died during World War I	accurately assess the distance of enemy targets
contour lines	show how high land is

close contour lines	symbols
replaced words	youth hostels, campsites or bus stations
symbols	sharply sloping land
explains symbols	key

LABEL

Label the information with the correct location year or event.

Board of Ordnance asked to survey	
revolution was happening in	
Ordnance Survey is an official mapping company for	
Ordnance Survey played significant role in	
topographers worked tirelessly from	
year of rebellion	

Label the information with the correct number.

Roy's age when he started mapping Scotland	
number of trained topographers in the company	
year in which Ordnance Survey began mapping during wartime	
percentage of maps in Britain Ordnance Survey produced by end of WWI	
number of Ordnance Survey staff who lost their lives during WWI	
number of Ordnance Survey maps supplied to the military by end of WWI	

Label the information with the correct location or event.

Maps provided a vital tool for	
show how high the land is	
Roy's map was known as	
length of time for Roy and his team to create the original map	
used instead of words	
map feature that explains what each symbol means	

👎👆 TRUE OR FALSE

Read the sentences. Put a tick in the correct box to show which sentences are *true* and which are *false*.

Britain's mapping agency was set up for military reasons.　True ☐　False ☐

The first Ordnance Survey maps were of parts of Scotland.　True ☐　False ☐

The Board of Ordnance mapped the south of England during the French Revolution.　True ☐　False ☐

William Roy was responsible for mapping the south of England.　True ☐　False ☐

The Great Map took eighty years to complete.　True ☐　False ☐

The Great Map recorded hills, roads, rivers and buildings.　True ☐　False ☐

Over fifty people were involved in mapping Scotland.　True ☐　False ☐

Roy used chains to measure distance.　True ☐　False ☐

Contour lines show how high the land is.　True ☐　False ☐

Roy was 21 years old when he started his map.　True ☐　False ☐

During the War, Ordnance Survey grew to a team of over 800 people.　True ☐　False ☐

Ordnance Survey produced 90 per cent of all war maps in Britain by 1915.　True ☐　False ☐

Ordnance Survey mapped trench positions, machine guns and batteries.　True ☐　False ☐

167 members of the Ordnance Survey team died during the war.　True ☐　False ☐

Ordnance Survey's primary role was to create maps that could be used once the war was finished.　True ☐　False ☐

◉ MULTIPLE CHOICE

Circle the correct answer for each of the following questions.

What do Ordnance Survey maps use instead of words?

| photos | lists | symbols | videos |

What do contour lines that are close together show?

| steep land | flat land | narrow roads | rivers |

How many Ordnance Survey staff members died during World War I?

| 76 | 87 | 78 | 67 |

What was the primary purpose of Ordnance Survey maps on the front line?

| assess distances | show pubs | find enemy tanks | plan buildings |

How many maps had been supplied by the end of World War I?

| almost 23 million | almost 20 million | 30 million | 33 million |

Ordnance Survey grew from a team of eight to how many?

| over 700 people | over 800 people | over 900 people | over 1,000 people |

In which war did Ordnance Survey play a significant role?

| the Great War | World War I | World War II | both World Wars |

Which of the following is used to explain the meaning of symbols on a map?

| words | glossary | contents | key |

How old was Roy when he began his military survey of Scotland?

| 20 | 21 | 22 | 23 |

Which area did the Board of Ordnance survey during the French Revolution?

| Scotland | eastern coasts | France | southern coasts |

Look at *Ordnance Survey maps*. Number the statements from 1 to 5 to show the order they occur in the text. Look at the first line of each paragraph to help you.

The maps often also use symbols instead of words to label features and make the maps clearer: as there are so many features, there wouldn't be enough space to note everything in words.

Nowadays, it may seem usual for a map to show hills, roads and water bodies.

The Ordnance Survey played a significant role in Britain's World War I and World War II campaigns.

The company name, 'Ordnance Survey', hints at how it began.

William Roy, a 21-year-old engineer, was asked to conduct the military survey of Scotland.

Look at the 'Modern Ordnance Survey maps' section in *Ordnance Survey maps*. Number the statements from 1 to 5 to show the order they occur in the text.

When contour lines appear close together, this means the land slopes sharply and would be steep to climb.

Ordnance Survey maps continue to be innovative, though, and offer much more.

The symbols could be small pictures, letters, lines or coloured areas, and they show features such as campsites, youth hostels, historic sites and bus stations.

If you have a chance to look at a map of your region, try studying its tiny details for yourself.

Contour lines are a way of showing on a map how high the land is.

Look at *Ordnance Survey maps*. Number the statements from 1 to 5 to show the order they occur in the text.

By the end of the war they had supplied almost 20 million maps, plans and diagrams to the military, providing a vital tool for the war effort.

When contour lines appear close together, this means the land slopes sharply and would be steep to climb.

The first Ordnance Survey maps were created following a rebellion in 1745, when the military realised it didn't have a detailed enough understanding of the land in Scotland for planning battles and moving troops.

It took him eight years to complete.

The company was no longer a small team of men with chains, but over 800 trained topographers (map-planners), observers, draughtsmen and printers.

FIND AND COPY

These questions are about *Ordnance Survey maps*.

Look at paragraph one. Find and copy a word that suggests that Ordnance Survey need to update their maps regularly.

_____

Look at 'Why were Ordnance Survey maps first made?' section. Find and copy a word that suggests people were not happy with the people who were ruling.

_____

Look at 'Who began the mapping?' section. Find and copy a word that suggests the maps identified roads and buildings.

_____

Look at 'Who began the mapping?' section. Find and copy a word that suggests that people worked together.

_____

Look at the paragraph beginning 'Ordnance Survey played a significant role…'. Find and copy a word that suggests that the Ordnance Survey workers were skilled and educated.

_____

Look at the paragraph beginning 'Ordnance Survey played a significant role…'. Find and copy a word that suggests that the Ordnance Survey were extremely hard working.

_____

Look at the paragraph beginning 'By 1915…'. Find and copy a word that suggests that the main role of Ordnance Survey staff was to work out how far away the enemy guns were.

_____

Look at the paragraph beginning 'Nowadays…'. Find and copy a word that suggests that Ordnance Survey is always thinking about new features they could add that haven't been used before.

_____

✎UNDERLINE OR HIGHLIGHT

Read the paragraphs below and then follow the instructions.

> The Ordnance Survey played a significant role in Britain's World War I and World War II campaigns. The company was no longer a small team of men with chains, but over 800 trained topographers (map-planners), observers, draughtsmen and printers. These people worked tirelessly from 1915 onwards, not only mapping the country but also plotting the positions of trenches, machine-guns and batteries belonging to the allies and the enemy.
>
> By 1915, Ordnance Survey was producing 90 per cent of all war maps. By the end of the war they had supplied almost 20 million maps, plans and diagrams to the military, providing a vital tool for the war effort. However, their primary role was actually to work on the front line of battle, to assess the distance of enemy artillery targets accurately. It was a dangerous job, and 67 members of the Ordnance Survey team lost their lives during World War I.

Underline or highlight a word that means a planned set of activities that bring about change.

Underline or highlight a word that means the main task you are employed to do.

Underline or highlight a word that means countries who support each other in war.

Underline or highlight a word that means marking the positions of things on a map.

Underline or highlight a word that means to refuse to give up or take a rest.

Underline or highlight a word that means narrow channels cut or dug into the ground.

Europe isn't a country but a continent. There are seven continents on Earth and each is divided into countries. Europe contains over 40 different countries, all of which have their own histories, traditions and cultures. France, Ukraine, Poland, Hungary, Norway and Spain are some of the countries in Europe.

Each individual country's culture is deeply rooted in different forms of art, architecture, literature, music, sport and even behaviour. Cultures have developed differently throughout Europe, while sharing some common themes.

Let's look at just a few of them.

German culture

German is the official language of Germany. Many other native languages are spoken too though, such as Polish, Kurdish and Danish, which shows how multi-cultural the country is. Many German classical musicians are world-famous, having composed some of the most recognisable concertos and symphonies in history. They include the composers Ludwig van Beethoven, Richard Wagner, Richard Strauss and Johann Sebastian Bach.

Sport in Germany is hugely important, too. The German men's football team has been ever-present in major competitions: they won World Cups in 1954, 1974, 1990 and 2014, and European Championships in 1972, 1980 and 1996. In motor sports, Michael Schumacher and Sebastian Vettel have also won eleven Formula 1 World Championships between them.

Some of Germany's most famous exported foods are its delicious sausages: bratwurst, currywurst, bockwurst – and many more! Germany is also world-famous for its beer. Both sausages and beer are celebrated at its annual festival Oktoberfest.

Danish culture

When you hear 'Denmark', you may think immediately of Vikings: fierce warriors who savagely invaded and raided other countries. However, Denmark nowadays has a strong culture promoting the arts and intellectual pursuits. Theatre, music, sculpture, photography and film receive large amounts of government funding in comparison to other countries. Involvement in the arts is believed to have a great positive impact on people's happiness.

Cycling also plays a major role in many Danes' lives. In many cities, cycle lanes are clear and wide, meaning people can cycle as a mode of transport, cycle for fun and train to cycle competitively for teams. Over 1.3 million people cycle in the city of Copenhagen each day, while Odense was named 'bicycle city of the year' for its 350-kilometre network of cycle lanes.

Greek culture

When you think of Greece, you might think of its ancient legends: perhaps of Zeus, the king of the gods; Poseidon, god of the seas; and Hades, god of the underworld. Perhaps you think about the stories of the Trojan War, Theseus and the Minotaur, or Cerberus, the three-headed dog who guarded the gates of hell. Greek culture certainly remembers its mythical past, but strongly embraces the present.

Greece holds the record for the most gold medals won at the Olympics per person in the population, and its basketball team is successful: they even beat the USA's 'dream team' in the 2006 World Cup.

Greece is also famous for its cuisine. Fresh fish from the Mediterranean sea, sun-ripened vegetables, creamy feta cheese and lashings of olive oil also make it one of the healthiest in the world.

Symbols of culture

European culture is recognised around the world and is symbolised by some historic, iconic buildings. The Colosseum in Rome, Italy, symbolises military and theatrical prowess. The Louvre Museum, in Paris, France, embodies the French love of art and all things beautiful. The Parthenon, in Greece, illustrates the country's respect for its ancient culture and gods. In London, United Kingdom, the Houses of Parliament and Buckingham Palace represent democracy and the royal family.

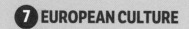

Read the sentences and choose the correct word or words to fill the gap.

Europe isn't a country, but a _____.

Europe contains over 40 different countries, all of which have their own histories, _____ and cultures.

Each individual country's culture is deeply rooted in different forms of art, _____, literature, music, sport and even behaviour.

Many other native languages are spoken too, though, such as Polish, _____ and Danish, which shows how multi-cultural the country is.

Many German _____ are world famous, having composed some of the most recognisable concertos and symphonies in history.

They include the composers _____, Richard Wagner, Richard Strauss and Johann Sebastian Bach.

_____ in Germany is hugely important, too.

Germany is also _____ for its beer.

When you hear 'Denmark', you may think immediately of _____: fierce warriors who savagely invaded and raided other countries.

Theatre, music, sculpture, photography and film receive large amounts of _____ funding in comparison to other countries.

Cycling also plays a major role in many _____ lives.

Greek culture certainly remembers its _____ past, but strongly embraces the present.

Greece is also famous for its cuisine. Fresh fish from the Mediterranean Sea, _____ vegetables, creamy feta cheese and lashings of olive oil also make it one of the healthiest in the world.

The _____ in Rome, Italy, symbolises military and theatrical prowess.

 MATCHING

Draw a line with a ruler to match the information.

German culture	Zeus and Hades
Danish culture	a continent
Greek culture	Polish, Kurdish and Danish languages
Europe	Viking links

Greek culture	arts, theatre and culture
Danish culture	Greece
German culture	Trojan War
the Parthenon	classical musicians

olive oil	German culture
cycling	London
motor sports	Danish culture
Houses of Parliament	Greek culture

Danish culture	the Colosseum, Rome
Greek culture	Beethoven and Bach
German culture	Mediterranean sea
symbol of culture	government funding for the arts

Theseus	London
Paris	sausages
royal family	the Louvre
exported food	Minotaur

LABEL

Label the information with the correct culture.

1.3 million people cycle in Copenhagen each day	
Cerberus the three-headed dog	
Michael Schumacher and Sebastian Vettel	
use olive oil in cooking	
has many gods	
love of art and all things beautiful	

Label the person or place with the correct country of origin.

Wagner, Bach and Strass	
Buckingham Palace	
Odense 'bicycle city of the year'	
Poseidon, god of the sea	
the Colosseum	
the Louvre	

Label the description with the correct information.

celebrated at Oktoberfest	
bicycle city of the year	
number of different countries in Europe	
Michael Schumacher and Sebastian Vettel won 11	
name of the mythical Greek war	
country where the Houses of Parliament are found	

🥊 TRUE OR FALSE

Read the sentences. Put a tick in the correct box to show which sentences are *true* and which are *false*.

There are over 50 countries in Europe.   True ☐   False ☐

Hungary is a country found in Europe.   True ☐   False ☐

Europe is a country.   True ☐   False ☐

Ukraine is a country found in Europe.   True ☐   False ☐

Kurdish is spoken in Germany.   True ☐   False ☐

Michael Schumacher is from Denmark.   True ☐   False ☐

Over 2 million people cycle in Copenhagen each day.   True ☐   False ☐

Polish is spoken in Germany.   True ☐   False ☐

Germany has many famous classical musicians.   True ☐   False ☐

The Parthenon is in Paris.   True ☐   False ☐

The Houses of Parliament are in Odense.   True ☐   False ☐

The Colosseum is in Rome.   True ☐   False ☐

Odense is a city in Denmark.   True ☐   False ☐

A bratwurst is a type of bicycle.   True ☐   False ☐

Danish citizens are heavily involved in the arts.   True ☐   False ☐

◉ MULTIPLE CHOICE

Circle the correct answer for each of the following questions.

How many countries are there in Europe?

over 30	over 40	over 50	over 60

When did the German men's football team first win the World Cup?

1947	1954	2014	1958

Which culture traditionally eats currywurst?

Danish	Scottish	German	Greek

Which culture believes in the positive impact of the arts?

Greek	German	Italian	Danish

How many Formula 1 titles have been won by Schumacher and Vettel?

11	12	13	14

The Greek basketball team beat which other nation's team in the 2006 World Cup?

Italy	USA	Germany	France

Which of the following is a symbol of military prowess?

Louvre Museum	Houses of Parliament	Colosseum	Parthenon

Which culture is famous for its use of olive oil?

Greek	German	Norwegian	Danish

Which culture places a lot of importance on cycling?

Greek	German	Norwegian	Danish

Which culture is known for its famous classical musicians?

Greek	German	Italian	Danish

123 SEQUENCING

Look at *European culture*. Number the statements from 1 to 5 to show the order they occur in the text. Look at the first line of each paragraph to help you.

German is the official language of Germany. ☐

Europe isn't a country, but a continent. ☐

European culture is recognised around the world and is symbolised by some historic, iconic buildings. ☐

Cycling also plays a major role in many Danes' lives. ☐

Some of Germany's most famously exported foods are its delicious sausages: bratwurst, currywurst, bockwurst – and many more! ☐

Look at the final paragraph in *European culture*. Number the statements from 1 to 5 to show the order they occur in the text.

The Parthenon, in Greece, illustrates the country's respect for its ancient culture and gods. ☐

European culture is recognised around the world and is symbolised by some historic, iconic buildings. ☐

In London, the Houses of Parliament and Buckingham Palace represent democracy and the royal family. ☐

The Colosseum in Rome, Italy, symbolises military and theatrical prowess. ☐

The Louvre Museum, in Paris, France, embodies the French love of art and all things beautiful. ☐

Look at *European culture*. Number the statements from 1 to 5 to show the order they occur in the text.

In motor sports, Michael Schumacher and Sebastian Vettel have also won 11 Formula 1 World Championships between them. ☐

Greek culture certainly remembers its mythical past, but strongly embraces the present. ☐

Europe contains over 40 different countries, all of which have their own histories, traditions and cultures. ☐

They include the composers Ludwig Van Beethoven, Richard Wagner, Richard Strauss and Johann Sebastian Bach. ☐

The Parthenon, in Greece, illustrates the country's respect for its ancient culture and gods. ☐

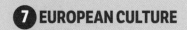

 FIND AND COPY

These questions are about _European culture_.

Look at paragraph one. Find and copy a word that suggests that continents are made up of more than one country.

_____

Look at the 'German culture' section. Find and copy a word that suggests the music that classical musicians wrote was familiar and well-known.

_____

Look at the 'German culture' section. Find and copy a word that suggests that musicians wrote music.

_____

Look at the 'German culture' section. Find and copy a word that suggests that German food is eaten in lots of other countries.

_____

Look at the 'German culture' section. Find and copy a word that suggests that Oktoberfest happens every year.

_____

Look at the 'Danish culture' section. Find and copy a word that suggests that the Vikings took things from other places.

_____

Look at the 'Greek culture' section. Find and copy a word that suggests that Cerberus protected hell.

_____

Look at the 'Symbols of culture' section. Find and copy a word that suggests that the Parthenon shows others about Greece's respect for the gods.

_____

✏ UNDERLINE OR HIGHLIGHT

Read the paragraphs below and then follow the instructions.

German is the official language of Germany. Many other native languages are spoken too, though, such as Polish, Kurdish and Danish, representing how multi-cultural the country is. Many German classical musicians are world famous, having composed some of the most recognisable concertos and symphonies in history. They include the composers Ludwig Van Beethoven, Richard Wagner, Richard Strauss and Johann Sebastian Bach.

Sport in Germany is hugely important, too. The German men's football team has been ever-present in major competitions: they won World Cups in 1954, 1974, 1990 and 2014, and European Championships in 1972, 1980 and 1996. In motor sports, Michael Schumacher and Sebastian Vettel have also won 11 Formula 1 World Championships between them.

Some of Germany's most famously exported foods are its delicious sausages: bratwurst, currywurst, bockwurst – and many more! Germany is also world-famous for its beer. Both sausages and beer are celebrated at its annual festival Oktoberfest.

Underline or highlight a word that means approved by a country's government.

Underline or highlight a word that means a very pleasant taste.

Underline or highlight a word that means honoured and marked publicly.

Underline or highlight a word that means linked to a particular place..

Underline or highlight a word that means sold to other countries.

Underline or highlight a word that means someone who plays an instrument as a hobby or job.

A solar system is a sun and the planets that move around it. Our solar system contains eight planets. Not all have been explored fully, but scientists and experts have managed to piece together a range of facts to help us understand them.

Mercury

Mercury is the smallest planet in the Solar system, only a little bigger than Earth's moon. It is the closest to the Sun but not the hottest – and it's still a staggering 57 million kilometres away. It takes around 88 Earth days to complete a round journey or 'orbit' around the Sun (which takes Earth a year). This is the shortest time of any planet in the Solar system. However one full rotation (which is how we measure a day on Earth) lasts almost 59 Earth days.

Venus

Venus has extreme temperatures and acidic clouds, which make the existence of life there unlikely. It is the hottest of the planets, with a surface temperature of around 460°C. A year for Venus takes 224.7 Earth days, and a day lasts almost the same amount of time: 243 Earth days. Unusually, Venus's rotation is in the opposite direction to Earth's.

Earth

The fifth largest planet in the solar system, our planet is the only one we know is inhabited by living things and the only one we know has liquid water. Earth is around 150 million kilometres from the Sun and takes 365 days to orbit it.

Mars

Mars is home to polar ice caps, extinct volcanoes and canyons. This planet – the fourth from the Sun – is well explored by humans. A day on Mars lasts just over 24 hours and it takes the planet 687 Earth days to orbit the Sun. It is known as the 'red planet' due to the rusty fragments of iron in its soil.

Jupiter

By far the largest planet in the solar system, Jupiter is twice as big as all of the other planets combined. It has 79 moons. A day lasts about ten Earth hours but a year takes about 12 Earth years. Jupiter is made mostly of hydrogen and helium: it does not have a solid surface, so spacecraft would be unable to land. Its extreme pressures and temperatures would also destroy any vehicle.

Saturn

Similar to Jupiter, Saturn is mainly made up of hydrogen and helium. Perhaps its most famous feature is its many rings, which are made of ice and rock. Saturn is believed to have a total of 62 moons. Although Saturn itself cannot support life similar to that on Earth, some of its moons are believed to have conditions that may support it. A year on Saturn lasts around 29.5 Earth years, and a day lasts almost 11 hours.

Uranus

Uranus is four times wider than Earth. It takes about 84 Earth years to complete a full orbit of the Sun, and about 17 hours to rotate once. Similar to Venus, Uranus's rotation is in a direction opposite to that of most planets. Uniquely, Uranus rotates on its side.

Neptune

Almost 30 times as far away from the Sun as Earth is, Neptune is the most distant planet in the solar system. Neptune, which was not discovered until 1846, is not visible to the naked eye from Earth. It takes about 16 Earth hours to rotate once, but around 165 Earth years to orbit the Sun, meaning it has so far completed only one rotation since its discovery. It has 13 moons and six known rings. Due to its icy properties, it would not be able to support life as we know it.

✏️ FILL IN THE GAP

Read the sentences and choose the correct word or words to fill the gap.

Our Solar system contains _____ planets.

Not all have been _____ fully, but scientists and experts have managed to piece together a range of facts to help us understand them.

Mercury is the smallest planet in the Solar system, only a little bigger than Earth's _____.

It is the _____ to the Sun, but not the hottest – and it's still a staggering 57 million kilometres away.

Venus has extreme temperatures and _____ clouds, which make the existence of life there unlikely.

Unusually, Venus's rotation is in the _____ direction to Earth's.

A day on Mars lasts just over 24 hours, and it takes the planet 687 Earth days to _____ the Sun.

It is known as the 'red planet' due to the rusty fragments of _____ in its soil.

A day lasts about _____ Earth hours, but a year takes about 12 Earth years.

Jupiter is made mostly of hydrogen and helium: it does not have a solid surface, so _____ would be unable to land.

Saturn is believed to have a total of _____ moons.

It takes about 84 Earth years to complete a full orbit of _____, and about 17 hours to rotate once.

Almost 30 times as far away from the Sun as Earth is, _____ is the most distant planet in the Solar system.

It takes about 16 Earth hours to rotate once, but around 165 Earth years to orbit the Sun, meaning it has so far completed only one rotation since its _____.

Due to its icy _____, it would not be able to support life as we know it.

Comprehension Ninja 9–10 © Andrew Jennings, 2020

 MATCHING

Draw a line with a ruler to match the information.

Mercury	iron
Earth	hydrogen and helium
Mars	closest to the Sun
Saturn	fifth largest planet

Venus	four times wider than Earth
Jupiter	hottest planet
Uranus	not visible to the naked eye
Neptune	largest planet in the solar system

discovered in 1846	Jupiter
red planet	Mars
79 moons in total	Saturn
62 moons in total	Neptune

destroy any vehicle	Neptune
165 years to orbit the Sun	Venus
smallest planet	Jupiter
rotation is opposite direction to Earth	Mercury

Earth	eight planets
solar system	rings of ice and rock
Mercury	88 Earth days to orbit the Sun
Saturn	365 days to orbit the Sun

LABEL

Label the information with the correct planet.

closest planet to the sun	
the largest planet in the solar system	
has polar ice caps, extinct volcanoes and canyons	
made up of hydrogen and helium	
most distant planet in the solar system	
four times wider than Earth	

Label the information with the correct planet.

takes 84 years to orbit the Sun	
62 moons	
takes 687 days to orbit the Sun	
has liquid water	
called the 'red planet'	
some moons could support life	

Label the information with the correct planet.

has 79 moons	
rotates in the opposite direction to Earth	
has 13 moons	
discovered in 1846	
rotates on its side	
rings made of ice and rock	

 **TRUE OR FALSE**

Read the sentences. Put a tick in the correct box to show which sentences are *true* and which are *false*.

Mercury is the planet that is closest to the Sun.   True ☐ False ☐

Jupiter is the furthest planet from the Sun.   True ☐ False ☐

Earth is the fourth largest planet in the solar system.   True ☐ False ☐

Mars is known as the 'red planet'.   True ☐ False ☐

Saturn has rings made of metal.   True ☐ False ☐

The solar system consists of nine planets.   True ☐ False ☐

The Earth takes 365 days to orbit the Sun.   True ☐ False ☐

Mars is the smallest planet in the solar system.   True ☐ False ☐

Jupiter is the same size as the Earth.   True ☐ False ☐

Jupiter has a surface similar to the Earth.   True ☐ False ☐

Venus has extreme temperatures and acidic clouds.   True ☐ False ☐

Mercury is the hottest planet.   True ☐ False ☐

Mars is red because of the iron in its soil.   True ☐ False ☐

Venus rotates in the opposite direction to Earth.   True ☐ False ☐

Neptune was not discovered until 1846.   True ☐ False ☐

◎ MULTIPLE CHOICE

Circle the correct answer for each of the following questions.

Which planet takes 88 Earth days to orbit the Sun?

| Mercury | Mars | Neptune | Jupiter |

Which is the fourth planet from the Sun?

| Venus | Neptune | Jupiter | Mars |

Which is the most distant planet from the Sun in the solar system?

| Mars | Jupiter | Saturn | Neptune |

Which planet is four times wider than Earth?

| Jupiter | Saturn | Uranus | Neptune |

Which of the following is the only known planet with liquid water?

| Venus | Earth | Mars | Jupiter |

How many planets are there in our solar system?

| six | seven | eight | nine |

Which of the following is known as the 'red planet'?

| Mercury | Venus | Mars | Saturn |

Which planet has 79 moons?

| Mercury | Mars | Uranus | Jupiter |

Which planet rotates on its side?

| Earth | Neptune | Jupiter | Uranus |

Which planet rotates in the opposite direction to Earth?

| Mercury | Venus | Mars | Jupiter |

Look at *Planets in the solar system*. Number the statements from 1 to 5 to show the order they occur in the text. Look at the first line of each paragraph to help you.

The fifth largest planet in the Solar system, our planet is the only one we know is inhabited by living things and the only one we know has liquid water.

By far the largest planet in the solar system, Jupiter is twice as big as all of the other planets combined.

Similar to Jupiter, Saturn is mainly made up of hydrogen and helium.

Mercury is the smallest planet in the Solar system, only a little bigger than Earth's moon.

Almost 30 times as far away from the Sun as Earth is, Neptune is the most distant planet in the Solar system.

Look at the 'Saturn' section in *Planets in the solar system*. Number the statements from 1 to 5 to show the order they occur in the text.

A year on Saturn lasts around 29.5 Earth years and a day lasts almost 11 hours.

Similar to Jupiter, Saturn is mainly made up of hydrogen and helium.

Although Saturn itself cannot support life similar to that on Earth, some of its moons are believed to have conditions that may support it.

Saturn is believed to have a total of 62 moons.

Perhaps its most famous feature is its many rings, which are made of ice and rock.

Look at *Planets in the solar system*. Number the statements from 1 to 5 to show the order they occur in the text.

However one full rotation (which is how we measure a day on Earth) lasts almost 59 Earth days.

A year on Saturn lasts around 29.5 Earth years and a day lasts almost 11 hours.

Earth is around 150 million kilometres from the Sun and takes 365 days to orbit it.

A year for Venus takes 224.7 Earth days and a day lasts almost the same amount of time: 243 Earth days.

Jupiter is made mostly of hydrogen and helium: it does not have a solid surface, so spacecraft would be unable to land.

 FIND AND COPY

These questions are about *Planets in the solar system*.

Look at paragraph one. Find and copy two words that suggest that some of the world's most knowledgeable people are involved in space exploration.

_____

Look at the 'Mercury' section. Find and copy a word that suggests that Mercury is turning all the time.

_____

Look at the 'Venus' section. Find and copy a word that suggests that there is something odd about how Venus rotates.

_____

Look at the 'Earth' section. Find and copy a word that suggests that there are living things on Earth.

_____

Look at the 'Mars' section. Find and copy a word that suggests that Mars's volcanoes are no longer active or erupting.

_____

Look at the 'Saturn' section. Find and copy a word that suggests that Saturn is very much like Jupiter.

_____

Look at the 'Uranus' section. Find and copy a word that suggests that Uranus does something that no other planet does.

_____

Look at the 'Neptune' section. Find and copy a word that suggests that Neptune has icy features.

_____

UNDERLINE OR HIGHLIGHT

Read the paragraphs below and then follow the instructions.

Saturn

Similar to Jupiter, Saturn is mainly made up of hydrogen and helium. Perhaps its most famous feature is its many rings, which are made of ice and rock. Saturn is believed to have a total of 62 moons. Although Saturn itself cannot support life similar to that on Earth, some of its moons are believed to have conditions that may support it. A year on Saturn lasts around 29.5 Earth years and a day lasts almost 11 hours.

Neptune

Almost 30 times as far away from the Sun as Earth is, Neptune is the most distant planet in the Solar system. Neptune, which was not discovered until 1846, is not visible to the naked eye from Earth. It takes about 16 Earth hours to rotate once but around 165 Earth years to orbit the Sun, meaning it has so far completed only one rotation since its discovery. It has 13 moons and six known rings. Due to its icy properties, it would not be able to support life as we know it.

Underline or highlight a word that means an interesting part of something.

Underline or highlight a word that means to finish something.

Underline or highlight a word that means very far away.

Underline or highlight a word that means to enable something to live.

Underline or highlight a word that means something is thought to be true.

Underline or highlight a word that means to turn in a circular movement.

9 THE BLACK DEATH

What was the Black Death?

The Black Death, or 'bubonic plague', was an infectious disease, called a 'plague', caused by bacteria called 'yersinia pestis'. The disease caused painful swellings called 'buboes'. Records estimate that it killed 75–200 million people across Europe and Asia during only four years from 1347.

How did the plague infect people?

It is widely believed that the bacteria were spread by black rats. These rats, unlike grey and brown rats, preferred to live in close proximity to humans, rather than in sewers and cellars. They didn't pass on the disease directly though: they only carried the devilish creatures that were to blame.

The real culprits were fleas. They infected the rats, who would be bitten by other fleas, who would then bite other rats – and so spread the plague bacteria through a colony of rats. Because of where they lived, the rats passed the fleas to humans.

How did it spread?

The Black Death spread across cities, huge mountain ranges and even oceans to infect and kill more and more people. This was because, in the 1300s, trade routes across Europe were flourishing and transport ships were becoming bigger, faster and more easily available. Huge distances could be covered in relatively short periods of time.

It wasn't only humans who used them though; rats would travel aboard these huge vessels. The ships' speed meant that rats could survive entire voyages, allowing the disease to spread across the sea. The fleas would also embed themselves in the clothing of human beings, helping them to spread further.

The plague is believed to have originated from China and it was brought to Europe by the Mongols. As the Mongol army attacked the last Italian trading post in the Crimea, plague broke out. The Italians retreated to their ships and sailed home to Italy, unknowingly bringing death with them.

    Comprehension Ninja 9–10 © Andrew Jennings, 2020

Why did the plague seem unstoppable?

One reason that the plague raged for such a long time was that people didn't realise the threat before it was too late.

Fleas would only start to bite humans if the rat on which they lived died. The infected rat colonies would start to die from the plague themselves but only after ten to 14 days – and only then would the fleas move on to humans. People would fall ill three to five days after being bitten, and then die after another three to five days.

This meant it could take a total of 23 days from the first rat being bitten to the first human dying. Hundreds, if not thousands, of people could have been bitten and infected in that time. Doctors tried to isolate people who were ill, thinking the plague was spread by human contact – but this made no difference.

What stopped the plague in the end?

No one is entirely sure quite what stopped the Black Death. The most likely explanation is simply that so many people died, and their towns were so effectively avoided, that the fleas ran out of living hosts. Before this happened, though, the disease had killed between 30 per cent and 60 per cent of all the people in Europe.

However, there were some places in Europe that had been untouched by it. Iceland and Finland, for example, had very little trade and contact with mainland Europe because of their remoteness and small population sizes. These countries' temperature also had a role to play: the plague bacteria spread much more quickly in warmer climates. If it did reach their shores, Finland and Iceland's freezing temperatures would have helped kill the plague bacteria before they could spread far.

✏️ FILL IN THE GAP

Read the sentences and choose the correct word or words to fill the gap.

If it did reach their shores, _____ freezing temperatures would have helped kill the plague bacteria before they could spread far.

Iceland and Finland, for example, had very little trade and contact with mainland Europe because of their _____ and small population sizes.

However, there were some places in _____ that had been untouched by it.

Doctors tried to _____ people who were ill, thinking the plague was spread by human contact – but this made no difference.

Hundreds, if not thousands, of people could have been _____ and infected in that time.

The disease caused painful _____ called 'buboes'.

The infected rat _____ would start to die from the plague themselves, but only after ten to 14 days – and only then would the fleas move on to humans.

Fleas would only start to bite humans if the _____ on which they lived died.

As the Mongol army attacked the last _____ trading post in the Crimea, plague broke out.

The fleas would also embed themselves in the _____ of human beings, helping them to spread further.

This was because, in the 1300s, _____ across Europe were flourishing and transport ships were becoming bigger, faster and more easily available.

The Black Death, or 'bubonic plague' was an _____ disease, called a 'plague', caused by bacteria called 'yersinia pestis'.

It is widely believed that the _____ were spread by black rats.

The real _____ were fleas.

Because of where they _____, the rats passed the fleas to humans.

The plague is believed to have originated from _____ and it was brought to Europe by the Mongols.

 MATCHING

Draw a line with a ruler to match the information.

real culprits	grey and brown rats
believed that bacteria circulated by	yersinia pestis
bacteria	fleas
lived in sewers and cellars	black rats

lived on black rats	black rats
fleas embedded in	travelled on ships
lived close to humans	fleas
black rats	human clothing

plague origin	attacked Italian trading post
Black Death	black rats
Mongol army	China
fleas' preferred food source	bubonic plague

once all rats died	infected rat colonies
died after ten to 14 days	painful swellings
three to five days after being bitten	fleas began to bite humans
infected humans had	humans fall ill

deaths in Europe	freezing temperatures
escaped the plague	75–200 million people
bacteria spread quickly	warmer temperatures
killed bacteria	Iceland and Finland

Label the information with the correct name or number.

the bacteria that caused the Black Death	
rodent that circulated the disease	
creature that lived on black rats	
type of rat that lives in sewers and cellars	
suggested death toll	
alternative name for the bubonic plague	

Label the description with the correct information.

period when trade routes flourished	
fleas embedded themselves here	
origin of the plague	
location of the last Italian trading post	
number of days the infected rat colonies die after	
once no rats left alive, fleas feed on	

Label the information with the correct name or number.

once infected, humans would develop	
number of days humans would take to fall ill	
painful swellings were known as	
doctors tried to reduce plague spreading by	
european countries that were not affected	
temperatures that kill plague bacteria	

👎 TRUE OR FALSE

Read the sentences. Put a tick in the correct box to show which sentences are *true* and which are *false*.

The Black Death was caused by bacteria.　　　　　True ☐　False ☐

Black rats liked to live in cellars and sewers.　　　True ☐　False ☐

Grey and brown rats lived close to humans.　　　　True ☐　False ☐

Fleas carried the bacteria yersinia pestis.　　　　True ☐　False ☐

Rats helped circulate the Black Death disease.　　　True ☐　False ☐

The Black Death is also known as the bubonic plague.　True ☐　False ☐

Growing trade routes helped spread the bacteria.　　True ☐　False ☐

The Black Death only affected England and France.　　True ☐　False ☐

Rats died if they became trapped on a ship.　　　　True ☐　False ☐

The Black Death originated in Italy.　　　　　　　True ☐　False ☐

The Mongol army attacked an Italian trading post in Crimea.　True ☐　False ☐

Fleas preferred to bite humans.　　　　　　　　　True ☐　False ☐

Rat colonies would die 15-20 days after infection.　　True ☐　False ☐

Once infected, people would develop painful swellings.　True ☐　False ☐

Every country in Europe was affected by the plague.　　True ☐　False ☐

◎ MULTIPLE CHOICE

Circle the correct answer for each of the following questions.

It is widely believed that the bacteria was spread by…

| cellars | sewage | black rats | fleas |

Where did black rats prefer to live?

| in sewers | in cellars | in the streets | close to humans |

Who were the real culprits for spreading the disease?

| humans | fleas | black rats | cats and dogs |

Where did fleas like to embed themselves?

| ships | food | black rats | clothes |

Where did the Black Death originate?

| Italy | England | China | Europe |

How long did it take humans to fall ill after they had been bitten?

| two to three days | three to four days | three to five days | four to five days |

What made no difference to the spread of the disease?

| medicine | isolation | fresh air | burning infected bodies |

Which places were untouched by the plague?

| Germany and France | Ireland and Wales | Finland and Iceland | China and Italy |

What percentage of Europe's population was killed by the plague?

| 20 to 30 per cent | 30 to 50 per cent | 40 to 60 per cent | 30 to 60 per cent |

What helped to kill the plague bacteria?

| antibiotics | fire | freezing temperatures | isolation |

 Comprehension Ninja 9–10 © Andrew Jennings, 2020

123 SEQUENCING

Look at *The Black Death*. Number the statements from 1 to 5 to show the order they occur in the text. Look at the first line of each paragraph to help you.

The Black Death spread across cities, huge mountain ranges and even oceans to infect and kill more and more people.

It wasn't only humans who used them though; rats would travel aboard these huge vessels.

Fleas would only start to bite humans if the rat on which they lived died.

However, there were some places in Europe that had been untouched by it.

The Black Death, or 'bubonic plague', was an infectious disease called a 'plague', caused by bacteria called 'yersinia pestis'.

Look at the 'How did it spread?' section in *The Black Death*. Number the statements from 1 to 5 to show the order they occur in the text.

The fleas would also embed themselves in the clothing of human beings, helping them to spread further.

This was because, in the 1300s, trade routes across Europe were flourishing and transport ships were becoming bigger, faster and more easily available.

The plague is believed to have originated from China and it was brought to Europe by the Mongols.

As the Mongols army attacked the last Italian trading post in the Crimea, plague broke out.

It wasn't only humans who used them though; rats would travel aboard these huge vessels.

Look at *The Black Death*. Number the statements from 1 to 5 to show the order they occur in the text.

Doctors tried to isolate people who were ill, thinking the plague was spread by human contact – but this made no difference.

Records estimate that it killed 75–200 million people across Europe and Asia during only four years from 1347.

The Italians retreated to their ships and sailed home to Italy, unknowingly bringing death with them.

This was because, in the 1300s, trade routes across Europe were flourishing, and transport ships were becoming bigger, faster and more easily available.

Finland and Iceland's freezing temperatures would have helped kill the plague bacteria before they could spread far.

FIND AND COPY

These questions are about *The Black Death*.

Look at paragraph one. Find and copy a word that suggests that something is not known precisely.

_____

Look at the 'How did the plague infect people?' section. Find and copy a word that suggests that bacteria moved from one place to another.

_____

Look at the 'How did the plague infect people?' section. Find and copy a word that suggests that fleas moved from rats to humans.

_____

Look at the 'How did it spread?' section. Find and copy a word that suggests that trade routes were growing quickly.

_____

Look at the 'How did it spread?' section. Find and copy a word that suggests that the Italians moved back to their ships for safety.

_____

Look at the 'Why did the plague seem unstoppable?' section. Find and copy a word that suggests doctors put people on their own to try and stop the plague from spreading.

_____

Look at the 'What stopped the plague in the end?' section. Find and copy a word that suggests that some parts of Europe were not affected by the plague.

_____

Look at the 'What stopped the plague in the end?' section. Find and copy a word that suggests that Finland and Iceland were far away from mainland Europe.

_____

UNDERLINE OR HIGHLIGHT

Read the paragraphs below and then follow the instructions.

How did it spread?

The Black Death spread across cities, huge mountain ranges and even oceans to infect and kill more and more people. This was because, in the 1300s, trade routes across Europe were flourishing and transport ships were becoming bigger, faster and more easily available. Huge distances could be covered in relatively short periods of time.

It wasn't only humans who used them though; rats would travel aboard these huge vessels. The ships' speed meant that rats could survive entire voyages, allowing the disease to spread across the sea. The fleas would also embed themselves in the clothing of human beings, helping them to spread further.

The plague is believed to have originated from China and it was brought to Europe by the Mongols. As the Mongol army attacked the last Italian trading post in the Crimea, plague broke out. The Italians retreated to their ships and sailed home to Italy, unknowingly bringing death with them.

Underline or highlight a word that means a long journey on a ship.

Underline or highlight a word that means to move away from enemy forces.

Underline or highlight a word that means thriving and doing well.

Underline or highlight a word that means continue to live in difficult conditions.

Underline or highlight a word that means on a ship.

Underline or highlight a word that means a ship or a large boat.

10 MENTAL HEALTH

What is mental health?

In the same way that physical health is about the body, mental health is about the mind.

Someone's mental health is the measure of how they think and feel. Good mental health suggests that people can think clearly and cope well with their emotional states. It also suggests that they are aware of the way they behave and can usually control it. Many people believe that mental health is also a measure of happiness.

The 21st century has seen a significant rise in mental health problems being reported, especially by young people.

What are mental health problems?

Mental health problems can affect anyone, at any stage of their life – and, more often than not, they creep up on people. They can significantly affect people's moods and actions before people realise it.

Mental health problems can be inherited and they can be the result of a physical health problem. Many arise as a result of stress or emotional trauma such as a death, repeated abuse or experience of violence. In 2018, one survey found that 74 per cent of people went through periods when they felt so stressed they were overwhelmed or unable to cope.

It is also believed that lifestyle factors such diet, levels of exercise and social encounters can affect a person's mental health.

What defines a mental health disorder?

Many of the feelings associated with mental health disorders also occur commonly and naturally. For example, you may feel nervous before a test – but tests are logical causes for worry. When thoughts or feelings become a persistent problem they may be related to a mental health disorder.

The following are just a few of the many mental health problems that affect people.

Anxiety is a feeling of intense or prolonged fear or panic. In 2013, there were 8.2 million reported cases of anxiety in the UK. One in six young people reported experiencing it.

Comprehension Ninja 9–10 © Andrew Jennings, 2020

Anorexia and bulimia are eating disorders. Sufferers tend to worry about their weight to an unhealthy extent and persist in trying to lose weight. Girls are ten times more likely than boys to develop eating disorders.

Depression is a condition defined by extremely low mood and can also cause people to avoid activity. Depression is one of the most common mental health disorders reported.

Obsessive-compulsive disorder (OCD) can trigger relentlessly repeating thoughts, images or feelings. Sufferers may repeat actions over and over, for example washing their hands.

Who can help with mental health problems?

Treatment is available for the mind, just like the body. If you have questions or concerns about your mental health, some advice is available online from charities such as Mind. However, the first and most important step to take is to speak to someone you trust. You should then contact your regular or local doctor. Doctors have access to specialist mental health services and can refer patients so they receive the most suitable help.

How can we improve our mental health?

We should take care of our mental health as much as our physical health. There are many simple things that can be done to boost mental wellbeing.

- Make time for friendships. Shared experiences stop people feeling isolated and alone.

- Exercising your body will help your mind. Exercising releases natural 'happy' chemicals called endorphins. Endorphins fight stress and can relieve depression.

- Get out into nature. Fresh air, vitamin D from the sun and gentle exercise are all proven to lift moods. Even plants and animals in people's homes can help.

- Talk about your mental health. Many people, especially boys and men, are taught that discussing feelings is a sign of weakness. The opposite is true.

 FILL IN THE GAP

Read the sentences and choose the correct word or words to fill the gap.

Good mental health suggests that people can think clearly and _____ well with their emotional states.

The _____ has seen a significant rise in mental health problems being reported, especially by young people.

Mental health problems can affect anyone, at any stage of their life – and, more often than not, they _____ up on people.

They can significantly affect people's moods and actions before people _____ it.

Get out into _____.

Fresh air, _____ from the sun and gentle exercise are all proven to lift moods.

Exercising releases natural 'happy' _____ called endorphins.

Shared _____ stop people feeling isolated and alone.

If you have questions or concerns about your _____, some advice is available online from charities such as Mind.

Doctors have access to specialist mental health services and can refer _____ so they receive the most suitable help.

In the same way that physical health is about the body, _____ is about the mind.

Obsessive-compulsive disorder (OCD) can trigger _____ repeating thoughts, images or feelings.

_____ is one of the most common mental health disorders reported.

Sufferers tend to worry about their _____ to an unhealthy extent and persist in trying to lose weight.

_____ is a feeling of intense or prolonged fear or panic.

_____ fight stress and can relieve depression.

MATCHING

Draw a line with a ruler to match the information.

anxiety	repeating thoughts
depression	feeling of fear or panic
OCD	worry about weight
eating disorder	having an extremely low mood

eating disorder	girls ten times more likely to suffer
anxiety	obsessions
depression	avoid activity
OCD	8.2 million UK cases in 2013

common type of mental illness	OCD
washing the hands many times	anxiety
try to lose weight	depression
one in six young people	eating disorder

'happy' chemicals	Mind
first step	vitamin D
mental health charity	speaking to someone you trust
sun	endorphins

cause of poor mental health	shared experiences
2018 survey	emotional trauma
mental health problems	74 per cent of people felt stressed
stop isolation	can affect anyone

Label the description with the correct condition.

a feeling of fear or panic	
repeating thoughts, images or feelings	
feeling extremely low	
an eating disorder	
one in six young people experience it	
worry about weight	

Label the description with the correct information.

percentage of people who felt stressed in 2018	
'happy' chemicals	
mental health charity	
activity that releases 'happy' chemicals	
vitamin that the sun can provide	
having these in your home can improve wellbeing	

Label the description with the correct condition.

8.2 million cases across the UK	
result of emotional trauma	
relentlessly repeating thoughts	
girls ten times more likely to have this than boys	
one of the most common types of mental illness	
sufferers repeat actions over and over	

 **TRUE OR FALSE**

Read the sentences. Put a tick in the correct box to show which sentences are *true* and which are *false*.

Mental health is all about a person's emotional wellbeing.	True ☐	False ☐
Mental health affects how we feel and think.	True ☐	False ☐
The 21st century has seen a rise in reported mental health problems.	True ☐	False ☐
Mental health problems only affect adults.	True ☐	False ☐
Mental health problems are sometimes linked to stress.	True ☐	False ☐
In 2018, 47 per cent of people felt so stressed they couldn't cope.	True ☐	False ☐
Anxiety is an eating disorder.	True ☐	False ☐
Anorexia is ten times more likely to affect boys than girls.	True ☐	False ☐
Anxiety is a feeling of fear or panic.	True ☐	False ☐
One in six adults experience anxiety at some point.	True ☐	False ☐
Anorexia is a problem where you tend to worry about your weight.	True ☐	False ☐
There were 8.2 million cases of anxiety in 2013.	True ☐	False ☐
Depression is a very common mental illness.	True ☐	False ☐
Depression is where you have repeating thoughts.	True ☐	False ☐
People with OCD may repeat actions.	True ☐	False ☐

◉ MULTIPLE CHOICE

Circle the correct answer for each of the following questions.

Which century has seen a significant rise in mental health problems being reported?

| 19th century | 20th century | 21st century | 22nd century |

Which of the following is a mental health problem that is characterised by an intense feeling of fear or panic?

| anxiety | anorexia | depression | bulimia |

Which of the following is a mental health problem that is characterised by extreme low mood?

| anorexia | depression | OCD | depression |

Which of the following is a mental health problem that is known as an eating disorder?

| anxiety | bulimia | OCD | depression |

In which year were 74 per cent of people stressed and unable to cope?

| 2016 | 2017 | 2018 | 2019 |

Who can direct you to specialist mental health services?

| nurses | teachers | parents | doctors |

Which of the following can help your body to release natural 'happy' chemicals?

| diet | exercise | massage | talking |

Where can you get vitamin D from?

| plants | exercise | sun | food |

Which of the following is a mental health charity?

| Heart | Health | Happy | Mind |

Which of the following is a mental health problem that is characterised by repeating thoughts?

| anxiety | bulimia | OCD | depression |

123 SEQUENCING

Look at *Mental health*. Number the statements from 1 to 5 to show the order they occur in the text. Look at the first line of each paragraph to help you.

Mental health problems can affect anyone, at any stage of their life – and, more often than not, they creep up on people.

Many of the feelings associated with mental health disorders also occur commonly and naturally.

Someone's mental health is the measure of how they think and feel.

Treatment is available for the mind, just like the body.

We should take care of our mental health as much as our physical health.

Look at the 'What defines a mental health disorder?' section in *Mental health*. Number the statements from 1 to 5 to show the order they occur in the text.

Obsessive-compulsive disorder (OCD) can trigger relentlessly repeating thoughts, images or feelings.

When thoughts or feelings become a persistent problem, they may be related to a mental health disorder.

Anxiety is a feeling of intense or prolonged fear or panic.

Anorexia and bulimia are eating disorders.

Depression is a condition defined by extremely low mood and can also cause people to avoid activity.

Look at *Mental health*. Number the statements from 1 to 5 to show the order they occur in the text.

Someone's mental health is the measure of how they think and feel.

Many people believe that mental health is also a measure of happiness.

When thoughts or feelings become a persistent problem, they may be related to a mental health disorder.

Endorphins fight stress and can relieve depression.

Many people, especially boys and men, are taught that discussing feelings is a sign of weakness.

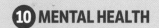

 **FIND AND COPY**

These questions are about _Mental health_.

Look at paragraph two. Find and copy a word that suggests how people deal well with their emotions.

_____

Look at paragraph three. Find and copy a word that suggests there has been a large increase in mental health problems.

_____

Look at 'What are mental health problems?'. Find and copy a word that suggests that people can receive mental health problems from their parents.

_____

Look at 'What are mental health problems?'. Find and copy a word that suggests some problems can make people feel like it is all too much to deal with.

_____

Look at 'What defines a mental health disorder?'. Find and copy a word that suggests that people may worry before a test.

_____

Look at 'What defines a mental health disorder?'. Find and copy a word that suggests that thoughts or feelings keep happening.

_____

Look at the paragraph beginning 'Depression'. Find and copy a word that suggests that depression might cause people to not want to exercise.

_____

Look at the paragraph beginning 'Obsessive-compulsive disorder'. Find and copy a word that suggests that some thoughts can feel like they will never stop happening.

_____

UNDERLINE OR HIGHLIGHT

Read the paragraphs below and then follow the instructions.

What defines a mental health disorder?

Many of the feelings associated with mental health disorders also occur commonly and naturally. For example, you may feel nervous before a test – but tests are logical causes for worry. When thoughts or feelings become a persistent problem, they may be related to a mental health disorder.

The following are just a few of the many mental health problems that affect people.

Anxiety is a feeling of intense or prolonged fear or panic. In 2013, there were 8.2 million reported cases of anxiety in the UK. One in six young people reported experiencing it.

Anorexia and bulimia are eating disorders. Sufferers tend to worry about their weight to an unhealthy extent and persist in trying to lose weight. Girls are ten times more likely than boys to develop eating disorders.

Depression is a condition defined by extremely low mood and can also cause people to avoid activity. Depression is one of the most common mental health disorders reported.

Obsessive-compulsive disorder (OCD) can trigger relentlessly repeating thoughts, images or feelings. Sufferers may repeat actions over and over, for example washing their hands.

Underline or highlight a word that means when things are connected with each other.

Underline or highlight a word that means to give information about something, often in a newspaper.

Underline or highlight a word that means something follows the rules of logic; it is sensible.

Underline or highlight a word that means a problem which affects mind or body.

Underline or highlight a word that means a very strong feeling of fear which makes you act without thinking.

Underline or highlight a word that means something continues to happen for a long time.

11 RECYCLING

Recycling is the process of turning used materials and waste into new products. A lot of our household waste can be broken down and reprocessed to make new things: this process uses less energy and fewer resources than making new items does.

Recycling is one of the most important ways that we can do our bit to preserve our planet, and to make sure it's a healthy place to live.

Non-recycled waste

Huge amounts of waste go to landfill sites. These are sites designated for dumping all sorts of solid waste into huge holes in the ground, which are eventually filled in. Anything and everything is dumped in them, including waste from homes, industry, farms and manufacturing.

As the contents of the landfill begin to degrade and rot, the gases they create can pollute the air. Of these gases, methane is the most serious. It often seeps into houses near landfill sites, and can cause explosions. Much of the material in landfill, though, barely degrades: plastics can take up to 1,000 years to break down.

Plastic and the ocean

Millions of tons of plastic enter the ocean every year. Plastic litter dropped on the floor is blown by the wind and washed by the rain into rivers and the sea.

Plastic products that are used in homes, such as cotton buds, wet wipes and cosmetics containing micro-beads, are washed down our drains and into the ocean (although micro-beads have now been banned in the United Kingdom).

Plastic waste is also dumped into the sea illegally, often in huge quantities. The plastic can trap or be eaten by creatures at sea. Even if it doesn't, it can clog and destroy their habitats.

Recycling innovations

In the UK, you may have seen recycling bins in city centres next to regular waste bins. You may have seen adults choosing paperless billing or used digital rather than paper resources at school. All of these innovations help to reduce landfill waste.

Comprehension Ninja 9–10 © Andrew Jennings, 2020

In Denmark, nearly 3,000 shops have reverse vending machines where customers can return bottles and cans that are then collected by a recycling company. They are recycled, melted and turned into new bottles and cans. The machine rewards the customer by refunding money from the original purchase. Perfect! The customer and the environment both benefit.

In Germany, glass bottles are returned to factories, washed and then reused – without recycling. This saves even more energy, resources and money.

Recycling at home

Everyone can make a difference. The five 'R's are a sensible place to start!

- Refuse: Don't buy things you don't need.

- Reduce: Buy products with minimal plastic packaging.

- Refill: Buy reusable bottles, travel cups and food containers rather than accepting new packaging.

- Re-use: Donate clothes, save carrier bags and wash out glass jars so they can be used again.

- Repair: If something breaks, repair it rather than replacing it.

You can also follow these tips for recycling at home.

- Find out from your council what day your recycling will be collected. Gather as much as you can each week before that day.

- Make life easier for the collection team: flatten your cardboard boxes, crush your cans and fill your boxes or bags rather than using several.

- Check what plastics and metal objects your council accepts for recycling. It may be more than you realised.

- Remember that you can easily recycle most paper and cardboard: envelopes, wrapping paper, birthday cards, toilet roll tubes, drinks cartons and even phone books. Look out for plastic linings on cartons and foil on wrapping paper and cards though: these may not be accepted for recycling.

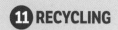 FILL IN THE GAP

Read the sentences and choose the correct word or words to fill the gap.

_____ is one of the most important ways that we can do our bit to preserve our planet and to make sure it's a healthy place to live.

_____: If something breaks, repair it rather than replacing it.

_____: Donate clothes, save carrier bags and wash out glass jars so they can be used again.

In _____, nearly 3,000 shops have reverse vending machines where customers can return bottles and cans that are then collected by a recycling company.

Plastic products that are used in homes, such as _____, wet wipes and cosmetics containing micro-beads, are washed down our drains and into the ocean (although micro-beads have now been banned in the United Kingdom).

The machine _____ the customer by refunding money from the original purchase.

_____: Buy reusable bottles, travel cups and food containers rather than accepting new packaging.

Plastic waste is also dumped into the sea _____, often in huge quantities.

Check what plastics and _____ your council accepts for recycling.

_____: Don't buy things you don't need.

Make life easier for the collection team: _____ your cardboard boxes, crush your cans and fill your boxes or bags rather than using several.

As the contents of the landfill begin to _____ and rot, the gases they create can pollute the air.

_____: Buy products with minimal plastic packaging.

Huge amounts of waste go to _____ sites.

Much of the material in landfill, though, barely degrades: plastics can take up to _____ to break down.

 **MATCHING**

Draw a line with a ruler to match the information.

flatten	site for dumping rubbish
reduce	plastic
landfill	cans
crush	cardboard boxes

recycling	don't buy things you don't need
refuse	council
reduce landfill waste	turning waste into new products
check recycling day	paperless billing

micro-beads	most paper and cardboard
easily recycled	Denmark
refill	banned by the UK government
reverse vending machines	bottles, travel cups and food containers

blown into the sea	reverse vending machine
plastic waste	donate clothes or save carrier bags
refunds money for bottles	eaten by animals
re-use	plastic litter

methane	if something breaks, fix it
repair	landfill contents
degrade and rot	creates gases
landfill	most serious gas

 **LABEL**

Label the statements with the correct information.

a process which turns waste into new products	
huge amounts of waste go here	
pollutes the air	
most serious gas	
recycling uses less	
type of waste that is dumped in landfills	

Label the statements with the correct information.

flatten before placing in recycling	
plastic is dumped here illegally	
how much plastic enters the ocean every year	
item banned by the UK government	
country with reverse vending machines	
number of shops with reverse vending machines	

Label the description with the correct 'R' word.

wash out glass jars	
don't buy things you don't need	
buy products with minimal plastic packaging	
fix things that break	
donate clothes, save carrier bags	
use bottles again rather than buying another	

 **TRUE OR FALSE**

Read the sentences. Put a tick in the correct box to show which sentences are *true* and which are *false*.

Sentence	True	False
Recycling is turning waste into new things.	☐	☐
A lot of our household waste can be reprocessed.	☐	☐
Landfills are also known as recycling centres.	☐	☐
Recycling uses more energy than making something new.	☐	☐
Only certain items can go into a landfill.	☐	☐
The contents of landfills will never rot or degrade.	☐	☐
Landfills can produce terrible gases.	☐	☐
Methane is a serious and dangerous gas.	☐	☐
By recycling we can reduce the amount of waste in landfill.	☐	☐
Cardboard can't be recycled.	☐	☐
Plastic linings may not be accepted for recycling.	☐	☐
Phone books and birthday cards can be recycled.	☐	☐
Most metal items are non-recyclable.	☐	☐
Thousands of tons of plastic enter the ocean every year.	☐	☐
Plastic waste can often be eaten by sea animals.	☐	☐

◎ MULTIPLE CHOICE

Circle the correct answer for each of the following questions.

Where do huge amounts of waste end up?

recycling centres	the ocean	landfill	waste

As the contents of landfills degrade, they create…

gases	toxins	pollution	waste

Which is the most serious gas that landfill sites produce?

carbon monoxide	oxygen	hydrogen	methane

How many years does plastic take to break down in landfill?

700	800	900	1,000

Which of the following moves litter into the sea?

micro-beads	wind and rain	landfill	recycling centres

Which of the following has been banned by the UK government?

plastic bags	plastic bottles	micro-beads	cotton buds

Plastic that ends up in the oceans often destroys…

animals' habitats	the ocean	animals	the environment

Which country has 3,000 reverse vending machines?

UK	Germany	Denmark	Scotland

In which country are glass bottles returned to factories for reuse?

UK	Germany	Denmark	Scotland

How many 'Rs' can help support recycling efforts?

two	three	four	five

123 SEQUENCING

Look at *Recycling*. **Number the statements from 1 to 5 to show the order they occur in the text. Look at the first line of each paragraph to help you.**

In Germany, glass bottles are returned to factories, washed and then reused – without recycling.

Huge amounts of waste go to landfill sites.

As the contents of the landfill begin to degrade and rot, the gases they create can pollute the air.

In Denmark, nearly 3,000 shops have reverse vending machines, where customers can return bottles and cans that are then collected by a recycling company.

In the UK, you may have seen recycling bins in city centres, next to regular waste bins.

Look at the 'Recycling at home' section in *Recycling*. **Number the statements from 1 to 5 to show the order they occur in the text.**

Refuse: Don't buy things you don't need.

Refill: Buy reusable bottles, travel cups and food containers rather than accepting new packaging.

Look out for plastic linings on carton and foil on wrapping paper and cards, though: these may not be accepted for recycling.

Find out from your council what day your recycling will be collected.

Check what plastics and metal objects your council accepts for recycling. It may be more than you realised.

Look at *Recycling*. **Number the statements from 1 to 5 to show the order they occur in the text.**

The customer and the environment both benefit.

Recycling is the process of turning used materials and waste into new products.

Much of the material in landfill, though, barely degrades: plastics can take up to 1,000 years to break down.

This saves even more energy, resources and money.

Plastic waste is also dumped into the sea illegally, often in huge quantities.

 **FIND AND COPY**

These questions are about *Recycling*.

Look at paragraph one. Find and copy a word that suggests that some materials are no longer wanted by anyone.

_____

Look at paragraph two. Find and copy a word that suggests that humans can do something to help keep the planet in a positive state.

_____

Look at the 'Non-recycled waste' section. Find and copy a word that suggests that certain places are chosen for the dumping of waste.

_____

Look at the 'Non-recycled waste' section. Find and copy a word that suggests that while in landfill, some waste begins to break down.

_____

Look at the 'Plastic and the ocean' section. Find and copy a word that suggest that it is against the law to dump waste into the sea.

_____

Look at the paragraph beginning 'In the UK…'. Find and copy a word that suggests that digital resources can help make less landfill waste.

_____

Look at the paragraph beginning 'In Denmark…'. Find and copy a word that suggests that you can get your money back when you return a bottle.

_____

Look at the 'Recycling at home' section. Find and copy a word that suggests that bottles can be filled again, rather than thrown away.

_____

✏️UNDERLINE OR HIGHLIGHT

Read the paragraphs below and then follow the instructions.

Recycling innovations

In the UK, you may have seen recycling bins in city centres, next to regular waste bins. You may have seen adults choosing paperless billing, or used digital rather than paper resources at school. All of these innovations help to reduce landfill waste.

In Denmark, nearly 3,000 shops have reverse vending machines, where customers can return bottles and cans that are then collected by a recycling company. They are recycled, melted and turned into new bottles and cans. The machine rewards the customer by refunding money from the original purchase. Perfect! The customer and the environment both benefit.

In Germany, glass bottles are returned to factories, washed and then reused – without recycling. This saves even more energy, resources and money.

Underline or highlight a word that means someone who buys goods or services.

Underline or highlight a word that means a new thing or way of doing something.

Underline or highlight a word that means a business or service completed without needing paper.

Underline or highlight a word that means money that is returned in exchange for a product.

Underline or highlight a word that means to have the opposite function.

Underline or highlight a word that means to bring back.

Each year in July, more than 200 cyclists from 22 teams compete in an epic bicycle race across France: the Tour de France. The race winds its way through sprawling cities, cobbled streets, picturesque countryside and even snow-capped mountains to its climax in Paris. It is divided into stages of different lengths and with types of track.

The first race

The race was first held in July 1903 and was won by a French man, Maurice Garin. Over 100 years later, the Tour has become one of the most high-profile sporting events in the world.

Winning jerseys

Instead of medals, cyclists in the Tour de France are awarded jerseys for their achievements in different categories as the race goes on.

- The yellow jersey is awarded to the rider with the lowest total time of all the stages that have been raced so far. At the end, this cyclist is the winner of the Tour de France.

- The green jersey is awarded to the rider who has accumulated the most points by finishing high in individual stages of the race and winning sprints.

- The polka-dot jersey is awarded to the best-performing racer in stages where difficult hills and mountains are involved.

- The white jersey is awarded to the best-placed rider under 26 years of age at the end of each stage.

British icons of cycling

Philippa York, who competed as Robert Millar, was an early hero, winning the title 'King of the Mountain' for being best at cycling up the steep mountain inclines of the 1984 Tour de France – the first time a British rider won a Tour de France classification. York finished fourth overall, achieving the highest-ranked British position in the Tour de France for over 20 years.

Bradley Wiggins was the first Briton to win the Tour de France in 65 years, in 2012. Wiggins rode for Team Sky and won the race by over a minute. He also won an Olympic gold medal in the same year.

Mark Cavendish, unlike Wiggins, was a specialist sprint cycler. Some of the stages of the Tour de France are short, and so are better suited for riders like him. He won thirty individual stages of the Tour de France, and was awarded an MBE in 2011.

Chris Froome won four Tour de France titles for Team Sky, in 2013, 2015, 2016 and 2017. He also won the other two 'grand tour' European cycling races: the Vuelta a España, in 2017, and the Giro d'Italia, in 2018. He took bronze in the 2017 World Championships, and was given an OBE.

Allegations

The Tour de France hasn't always been known for glory, sporting greatness and human resilience. Some riders are apparently willing to do anything to win, and the sport has been rocked by allegations of cheating – mainly the use of performance-enhancing drugs.

One of these drugs is called EPO. EPO makes the body produce more red blood cells so it can absorb more oxygen. As a result, athletes can produce more energy for longer, giving them an unfair advantage.

Perhaps the most famous conviction for use of EPO was American cyclist Lance Armstrong's. He won seven Tour de France titles, but had all of them invalidated after he tested positive for the drug. After initially denying that he had used it, he finally admitted his sporting crimes on TV, in 2013.

Record winners

Winning the Tour de France is a dream that few riders achieve. However, winning once just wasn't enough for some! The table below shows the Tour's most prolific riders – some of whom won the prestigious title no less than five times. As you will notice, Lance Armstrong is no longer present on this list.

5	Jacques Anquetil	1957, 1961, 1962, 1963, 1964
	Eddy Merckx	1969, 1970, 1971, 1972, 1974
	Bernard Hinault	1978, 1979, 1981, 1982, 1983
	Miguel Indurain	1991, 1992, 1993, 1994, 1995
4	Chris Froome	2013, 2015, 2016, 2017
3	Phillipe Thys	1913, 1914, 1920
	Louison Bobet	1953,1954, 1955
	Greg LeMond	1986, 1989, 1990

✏ FILL IN THE GAP

Read the sentences and choose the correct word or words to fill the gap.

The white jersey is awarded to the best-placed rider _____ years of age at the end of each stage.

The _____ is awarded to the rider with the lowest total time of all the stages that have been raced so far.

The polka-dot jersey is awarded to the best-performing racer in stages where _____ and mountains are involved.

The green jersey is awarded to the rider who has accumulated the _____ by finishing high in individual stages of the race and winning sprints.

Perhaps the most famous _____ for use of EPO was American cyclist Lance Armstrong's.

EPO makes the body produce more red blood cells so it can absorb more _____.

He won seven Tour de France titles, but had all of them _____ after he tested positive for the drug.

Some riders are apparently willing to do anything to win, and the sport has been rocked by allegations of _____ – mainly the use of performance-enhancing drugs.

He won _____ individual stages of the Tour de France, and was awarded an MBE in 2011.

Some of the stages of the Tour de France are short, and so are _____ for riders like him.

Mark Cavendish, unlike Wiggins, was a _____ sprint cycler.

_____ won four Tour de France titles for Team Sky, in 2013, 2015, 2016 and 2017.

Over 100 years later, the tour has become one of the most _____ sporting events in the world.

The race winds its way through _____, cobbled streets, picturesque countryside and even snow-capped mountains to its climax in Paris.

Each year in July, more than _____ from 22 teams compete in an epic bicycle race across France: the Tour de France.

MATCHING

Draw a line with a ruler to match the information.

Bradley Wiggins	King of the Mountain 1984
Philippa York	Olympic gold medal winner
Mark Cavendish	specialist sprinter
Tour de France	world's most famous race

Giro d'Italia 2018	Mark Cavendish
MBE 2011	Chris Froome
July 1903	Bradley Wiggins
Tour de France 2012	first race

Chris Froome	1990
Jacques Anquetil	2013
Greg LeMond	never won
Mark Cavendish	1957

Lance Armstrong	best climber
green jersey	produces more red blood cells
EPO	seven Tour de France titles invalidated
polka-dot jersey	most points

yellow jersey	EPO
admitted cheating on TV	lowest total time
banned drug	best rider under 26
white jersey	Lance Armstrong

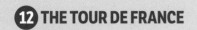

LABEL

Label the description with the correct cyclist.

won the Tour de France in 1991 and 1994	
specialist sprinter	
1984 King of the Mountain	
won the Tour de France by over a minute	
drugs cheat	
won the Tour de France in 1957 and 1961	

Label the description with the correct jersey.

winner of the Tour de France	
hills and mountains	
lowest total time	
most points accumulated	
under 26	

Label the year with the correct winner.

1986	
1920	
1994	
1971	
1954	
1981	

TRUE OR FALSE

Read the sentences. Put a tick in the correct box to show which sentences are *true* and which are *false*.

The Tour de France happens every year.   True ☐   False ☐

The Tour de France happens in Germany.   True ☐   False ☐

The Tour de France was first held in 2012.   True ☐   False ☐

Bradley Wiggins won the first Tour de France.   True ☐   False ☐

The race moves through cobbled towns and snowy mountains.   True ☐   False ☐

Lance Armstrong had seven Tour de France titles invalidated.   True ☐   False ☐

Mark Cavendish is a specialist sprinter.   True ☐   False ☐

Bradley Wiggins won the Olympics and Tour de France in the same year.   True ☐   False ☐

Chris Froome has won the Tour de France four times.   True ☐   False ☐

Mark Cavendish has won the Tour de France thirty times.   True ☐   False ☐

200 cyclists from 22 teams compete in the race.   True ☐   False ☐

The Tour de France is a car race.   True ☐   False ☐

People have used performance-enhancing drugs to try and win the race.   True ☐   False ☐

EPO builds larger muscles.   True ☐   False ☐

Lance Armstrong admitted to cheating on TV.   True ☐   False ☐

◉ MULTIPLE CHOICE

Circle the correct answer for each of the following questions.

In which month does the Tour de France take place?

| January | May | July | September |

How many teams compete in the Tour de France?

| 12 | 18 | 22 | 26 |

In which city does the Tour de France finish?

| London | Lyon | Paris | Brussels |

When was the Tour de France first held?

| 1991 | 1954 | 1918 | 1903 |

Which jersey is awarded to the best rider under the age of 26?

| green | white | yellow | polka-dot |

Which jersey is awarded to the rider who performs the best on difficult hills and mountains?

| green | white | yellow | polka-dot |

Who won the Tour de France in 1989?

| Jacques Anquetil | Bernard Hinault | Greg LeMond | Miguel Indurain |

Who won the Tour de France in 1992?

| Jacques Anquetil | Bernard Hinault | Greg LeMond | Miguel Indurain |

Which of the following cyclists admitted using EPO?

| Bradley Wiggins | Lance Armstrong | Phillipe Thys | Eddy Merckx |

What does EPO make the body produce more of?

| red blood cells | energy | oxygen | carbohydrates |

123 SEQUENCING

Look at *The Tour de France*. Number the statements from 1 to 5 to show the order they occur in the text. Look at the first line of each paragraph to help you.

The race was first held in July 1903, and was won by a French man, Maurice Garin.

The Tour de France hasn't always been known for glory, sporting greatness and human resilience.

Instead of medals, cyclists in the Tour de France are awarded jerseys for their achievements in different categories as the race goes on.

Perhaps the most famous conviction for use of EPO was American cyclist Lance Armstrong's.

Each year in July, more than 200 cyclists from 22 teams compete in an epic bicycle race across France: the Tour de France.

Look at the table in *The Tour de France*. Number the statements from 1 to 5 to show the order they appear in the table.

Chris Froome

Eddy Merckx

Miguel Indurain

Louison Bobet

Phillipe Thys

Look at *The Tour de France*. Number the statements from 1 to 5 to show the order they occur in the text.

He also won an Olympic gold medal in the same year.

One of these drugs is called EPO.

At the end, this cyclist is the winner of the Tour de France.

He also won the other two 'grand tour' European cycling races: the Vuelta a España, in 2017, and the Giro d'Italia, in 2018.

However, winning once just wasn't enough for some!

FIND AND COPY

These questions are about *The Tour de France*.

Look at paragraph one. Find and copy a word that suggests that teams are fighting against each other to win.

_____

Look at paragraph one. Find and copy a word that suggests that the race is very big and exciting.

_____

Look at the 'Winning jerseys' section. Find and copy a word that suggests that riders earn points in each stage.

_____

Look at the paragraph beginning 'Philippa York...'. Find and copy a word that suggests that the mountains are very tough to ride up.

_____

Look at the paragraph beginning 'Chris Froome...'. Find and copy a word that suggests that Chris Froome finished in third place in the 2017 World Championships.

_____

Look at the 'Allegations' section. Find and copy a word that suggests that cycling was negatively affected by cheating allegations.

_____

Look at the paragraph beginning 'Perhaps the most famous...'. Find and copy a word that suggests that Lance Armstrong's titles were taken away and no longer stand.

_____

Look at the paragraph beginning 'Winning the Tour de France...'. Find and copy a word that refers to the Tour's most successful riders.

_____

UNDERLINE OR HIGHLIGHT

Read the paragraphs below and then follow the instructions.

Allegations

The Tour de France hasn't always been known for glory, sporting greatness and human resilience. Some riders are apparently willing to do anything to win, and the sport has been rocked by allegations of cheating – mainly the use of performance-enhancing drugs.

One of these drugs is called EPO. EPO makes the body produce more red blood cells so it can absorb more oxygen. As a result, athletes can produce more energy for longer, giving them an unfair advantage.

Perhaps the most famous conviction for use of EPO was American cyclist Lance Armstrong's. He won seven Tour de France titles, but had all of them invalidated after he tested positive for the drug. After initially denying that he had used it, he finally admitted his sporting crimes on TV in 2013.

Underline or highlight a word that means fame for being impressive.

Underline or highlight a word that means stating that something is not true.

Underline or highlight a word that means to confess to something.

Underline or highlight a word that means able to recover easily from difficulty.

Underline or highlight a word that means improving or making better.

Underline or highlight a word that means breaking the rules in order to win.

13 THE BRITISH EMPIRE

The British Empire was, at its greatest extent, the largest empire the world has ever seen. It covered over six times more land than the Roman Empire and included almost seven times as many people.

It began relatively late in empires' history. Throughout the 16th century, England had been envious of Portugal's and Spain's established overseas empires, which had created great wealth and fame for both countries in the Americas.

Between the late 16th and 18th centuries, Britain expanded its trade network across the world. New trade ports meant new settlements, or 'colonies'. In 1607, Britain planned to establish trading and stock companies to manage colonisation attempts in North America. They were created to sell the gold, sugar, furs and people being traded in and out of the Americas. England's first permanent settlement was founded.

In 1670, the lucrative Hudson's Bay Company was created in what is now Canada, to gather and trade in the fur of moose, beaver, squirrel and even otter. 1672 saw the founding of perhaps the most shocking addition: the Royal African Company, which made money by taking slaves from Africa and selling them to British colonies in the Americas. Slavery was made illegal in Britain in 1807, but not across the Empire until 1834. By then, the Empire had transported over 3.5 million slaves across the Atlantic Ocean.

In total, 13 British colonies were established in North America – but by 1770 the relationship between the colonies and Britain had broken down. The 13 Colonies declared independence from Britain and formed the United States in 1776. Canada, however, remained loyal.

After losing control of the United States, Britain further explored Asia and Australia. In 1770, Captain James Cook claimed Australia for Britain. Colonies and farms were founded, but conditions were harsh. Seventeen years later, Britain decided to populate Australia by sending convicted British criminals to serve their sentences there. The amount of gold that they mined and the wool that they produced made Australia extremely profitable.

Comprehension Ninja 9–10 © Andrew Jennings, 2020

Asia was now Britain's next target. During the 1800s, the British East India Company, which specialised in the trade of tea, cotton, silk, salt and spices, was used to drive Britain's increasing influence. It imposed British rule across countries such as China, India, Hong Kong, Egypt and Burma. The British Army and British government outposts maintained control, suppressing local populations and meeting disobedience with violence.

The British Empire continued to grow until its peak in 1920, when it ruled almost 24 per cent of the world. It had already begun to weaken, though, due to war: first against Russia and then in World War I. Rebellions and uprisings increased, and the British Empire gradually began to shrink. Over the next 80 years, colonised countries gained their independence, either as a result of unrest or, in some cases, through goodwill.

India gained its independence from Britain on 15 August 1947 after many years of campaigning that was largely led by Mahatma Gandhi. In 1960, Cyprus regained independence, followed by Jamaica and Trinidad in 1961 and 1962. Barbados achieved it in 1966. In only 1997, Hong Kong became a Chinese region once again.

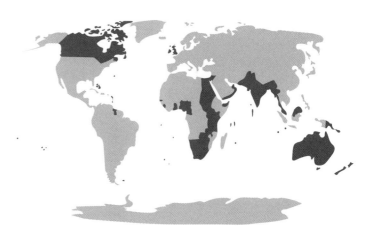

Nowadays, Britain has 14 overseas territories and is also part of the Commonwealth of Nations. This is made up of 53 countries that were almost all once ruled by the British Empire, including India, Canada and Australia. Sixteen of these countries still voluntarily regard the Queen of England as their head of state. Many still have British architecture, legal systems, sports, language and conventions – such as playing cricket, and driving on the left-hand side of the road.

🔵 FILL IN THE GAP

Read the sentences and choose the correct word or words to fill the gap. Refer back to
The British Empire **to find the correct answer.**

In total, 13 _____ were established in North America – but, by 1770, the relationship between the colonies and Britain had broken down.

During the 1800s, the British East India Company, which specialised in the trade of tea, cotton, silk, salt and spices, was used to drive Britain's increasing _____.

After losing control of the _____, Britain further explored Asia and Australia.

🔵 MATCHING

Draw a line with a ruler to match the information.

Captain James Cook •	• created in Canada
British East India Company •	• covered over six times more land than the Roman Empire
British Empire •	• claimed Australia for Britain
Hudson's Bay Company •	• drove Britain's influence

🔵 LABEL

Label the description with the correct year.

Cyprus regained independence	
British Empire peaked	
Hudson's Bay Company created	
United States was formed	
Captain Cook claimed Australia for Britain	
slavery made illegal in Britain	

🔵 TRUE OR FALSE

Read the sentences. Put a tick in the correct box to show which sentences are *true* and which are *false*.

Hong Kong became a Chinese region in 1997.	True ☐	False ☐
In its peak, Britain ruled almost 24 per cent of the world.	True ☐	False ☐
The British Empire began between the 15th and 17th centuries.	True ☐	False ☐
Conditions in 1770s Australia were excellent.	True ☐	False ☐
The British Army and British government suppressed local populations.	True ☐	False ☐

◎ MULTIPLE CHOICE

Circle the correct answer to the following question.

How many slaves did the British Empire transport across the Atlantic Ocean?

over 1.7 million	over 2.3 million	over 3.1 million	over 3.5 million

123 SEQUENCING

Look at *The British Empire*. Number the statements from 1 to 4 to show the order they occur in the text.

Nowadays, Britain has 14 overseas territories and is also part of the Commonwealth of Nations.	
In 1607, Britain planned to establish trading and stock companies to manage colonisation attempts in North America.	
In total, 13 British colonies were established in North America – but, by 1770, the relationship between the colonies and Britain had broken down.	
Between the late 16th and 18th centuries, Britain expanded its trade network across the world.	

🔍 FIND AND COPY

These questions are about *The British Empire*.

Look at the paragraph beginning 'After losing control of the United States…'. Find and copy a word that tells us that Australia helped make Britain lots of money.

_____

Look at the paragraph beginning 'Nowadays, Britain has 14 overseas territories…'. Find and copy a word that suggests that some countries regard the Queen as their head of state by choice.

_____

✎ UNDERLINE OR HIGHLIGHT

Read the paragraph below and then follow the instructions.

> In 1960, Cyprus regained independence, followed by Jamaica and Trinidad in 1961 and 1962. Barbados achieved it in 1966. In only 1997, Hong Kong became a Chinese region once again.

Underline or highlight a word that means to get something back which you had lost.

Underline or highlight a word that means to succeed in doing something.

J.K. Rowling is responsible for some of the biggest-selling books of all time – but there's probably a lot you don't know about the creator of the Harry Potter books and their wizarding world.

Joanne Rowling was born near Bristol on 31 July 1965. Growing up, she admits to being a real bookworm who loved to read, like her parents. She also developed a passion for writing from a very early age. Aged just six, she wrote her first story, about a rabbit. Five years later, she wrote her first novel – a tale of seven cursed diamonds.

After leaving school, Rowling studied French and Classics at the University of Exeter. Following this, she moved to London. Among several other jobs, she worked as a researcher at Amnesty International (an organisation that campaigns for human rights).

The idea for the Harry Potter books came while Rowling was sitting on a delayed train from Manchester to London King's Cross. Inspired, she began to plan the plot and all seven books in the series, creating piles and piles of scribbled notes. Soon afterwards, Rowling moved to Portugal to teach English. She married Jorge Arantes and the couple had a daughter, Jessica. When the marriage ended, she returned to the UK with Jessica and relocated to Edinburgh, in Scotland. By then, the first three chapters of *Harry Potter and the Philosopher's Stone* had been written.

Rowling sent these chapters to a number of literary agents, and was rejected. When she finally found an agent, the chapters were rejected again by publishers – 12 times! The one person who was hooked by Harry Potter was the eight-year-old daughter of an editor. She demanded to read the rest of the story, and the editor took another look.

In the subsequent years, more Harry Potter books were published – and many records were broken. In 2007, *Harry Potter and the Deathly Hallows* sold 2.65 million copies in the first 24 hours following its release. Fans rushed to shops at midnight – many of them wearing wizard costumes – to get their hands on the book. It soon became the fastest-selling book ever.

Since its astounding success, Rowling's series has been translated into over 75 languages (including Latin!), and fans from around the world have fallen in love with the boy wizard.

The Harry Potter books were, of course, accompanied by a series of films, which propelled many of its cast members – including Daniel Radcliffe and Emma Watson – to superstardom. Like the books, the films became a phenomenon and earned the stories even more fans.

Despite earning a cult following, Joanne proved she was not a one-trick pony when, in 2012, she published her first book for adults, *The Casual Vacancy*. She has also written a number of crime novels under the pseudonym Robert Galbraith.

She has never forgotten her wizarding world, however. In 2016, she collaborated with playwright Jack Thorne to write *Harry Potter and the Cursed Child*. The play soon became a must-see show in London's West End, with performances selling out months in advance.

Joanne also wrote the screenplay for the film *Fantastic Beasts and Where to Find Them*. Although the film does not feature Harry Potter himself, it's based within the same wizarding world. A sequel, *Fantastic Beasts: The Crimes of Grindelwald*, was released in 2018.

Over the years, Joanne has earned legions of fans and scores of awards for her work: the Booksellers Association Author of the Year, the Hans Christian Andersen Award and the Lifetime Achievement Award at the British Book Awards. She remains undoubtedly one of the UK's most popular writers.

✏️ FILL IN THE GAP

Read the sentences and choose the correct word or words to fill the gap. Refer back to *J.K. Rowling* to find the correct answer.

Inspired, she began to plan the plot and all _____ books in the series, creating piles and piles of scribbled notes.

Since its astounding success, Rowling's series has been _____ into over 75 languages (including Latin!), and fans from around the world have fallen in love with the boy wizard.

Over the years, Joanne has earned legions of fans and scores of awards for her work: the Booksellers Association Author of the Year, the Hans Christian Andersen Award and the _____ Achievement Award at the British Book Awards.

🔗 MATCHING

Draw a line with a ruler to match the information.

J.K. Rowling born	• •	Portugal
taught English	• •	Edinburgh
relocated to	• •	near Bristol
had the idea	• •	on a train

✂️ LABEL

Label the description with the correct year or number.

Harry Potter and the Cursed Child	
Fantastic Beasts: The Crimes of Grindelwald	
The Casual Vacancy	
Harry Potter and the Deathly Hallows released	
number of languages Harry Potter has been translated into	
number of times rejected by publishers	

✔️ TRUE OR FALSE

Read the sentences. Put a tick in the correct box to show which sentences are *true* and which are *false*.

Harry Potter's success is due to an editor's eight-year-old daughter.	True ☐	False ☐
J.K. Rowling was inspired to write during a train journey.	True ☐	False ☐
Harry Potter is now a popular West End show.	True ☐	False ☐
The Harry Potter films were not well liked.	True ☐	False ☐
Rowling moved to America to teach English.	True ☐	False ☐

◎ MULTIPLE CHOICE

Circle the correct answer.

How many copies of *Harry Potter and the Deathly Hallows* were sold in the first 24 hours after its release?

1.99 million	2.65 million	3.12 million	3.52 million

123 SEQUENCING

Look at *J.K. Rowling*. Number the statements from 1 to 4 to show the order they occur in the text.

Aged just six, she wrote her first story, about a rabbit.	
She remains undoubtedly one of the UK's most popular writers.	
She demanded to read the rest of the story, and the editor took another look.	
Like the books, the films became a phenomenon and earned the stories even more fans.	

◉ FIND AND COPY

These questions are about *J.K. Rowling*.

Look at paragraph two. Find and copy a word that suggests that J.K. Rowling loved writing when she was young.

_____

Look at the paragraph beginning 'Beginning…'. Find and copy a word that suggests that J.K. Rowling worked with someone else to write *The Cursed Child*.

_____

◐ UNDERLINE OR HIGHLIGHT

Read the paragraph below and then follow the instructions.

> Despite earning a cult following, Joanne proved she was not a one-trick pony when, in 2012, she published her first book for adults, *The Casual Vacancy*. She has also written a number of crime novels under the pseudonym Robert Galbraith.

Underline or highlight a word that means a large group of people who all feel or think the same way about something.

Underline or highlight a word that means a name used instead of your own.

15 RESIDENTIAL ACTIVITIES

Residential activities are activities that take place away from home, over several days. The experience may be the first time children spend a prolonged period of time away from their homes and families, and can form some of the most memorable and rewarding times of their lives.

Residential activity experiences are designed to give children the opportunity to participate in activities they wouldn't normally have the chance to try – activities that are designed to challenge them both mentally and physically.

Any of the following activities could be on offer. Use this handy fact file to choose which ones would suit you!

Abseiling

Abseiling is a mental and physical challenge. It involves using a hanging rope to move from high to low, usually from bridges or cliff edges to the ground. It's not for the faint hearted!

Fun Rating: ★★★★ Challenge Rating: ★★★★★

Archery

In archery, you use a bow to fire arrows at targets at a distance, trying to hit the bullseye. The rings around the bullseye award different numbers of points, which can make it a close contest!

Fun Rating: ★★★★★ Challenge Rating: ★★

Bushcraft

Bushcraft will teach you how to survive in the wild like a pro! You'll learn how to respect the forest while building shelters, creating simple tools and starting a bonfire – safely! It's great for team-building and building confidence.

Fun Rating: ★★★★ Challenge Rating: ★★★★

Crate climbing

Create a tower of terror! Working as a team, you use your coordination and balance to stack plastic crates – but you must be stood on top of the crates while you stack! When they finally collapse, your harness will keep you hanging.

Fun Rating: ★★★★★ Challenge Rating: ★★★★★

Orienteering

Fitness and fun are combined here! Orienteering is a race across a variety of land types. Using maps, you will need to find various points and record symbols. The first to gather the symbols and return to the beginning wins.

Fun Rating: ★★★ Challenge Rating: ★★★

Zip lines

Fast, furious and fun, the zip line takes you on for an adrenaline-filled ride! You hook into the harness and away you go, zipping through the air from one platform to the next. For next-level fun, try no hands!

Fun Rating: ★★★★★ Challenge Rating: ★★★★★

Night line

Trust, communication and teamwork are essential here, as you're blindfolded before you follow your guide rope through an assault course. You have to trust the instructions coming from the leader of your line to help you through.

Fun Rating: ★★★ Challenge Rating: ★★★★★

Kayaking

Kayaking is the perfect activity for practising your balance, rhythm and determination – but you have to be ready to get wet! With your one-person boat and oar, you'll brave the waves to keep up with the river.

Fun Rating: ★★★★★ Challenge Rating: ★★★

Forest adventure

The forest adventure will test all the new skills and knowledge you have gained. Dropped at an unknown point in the forest, you have to use bushcraft and navigation skills to find your way back to base. Can your team return safely?

Fun Rating: ★★ Challenge Rating: ★★★

How well would you do on a residential experience? Even if you're doubtful of your abilities now, things could change. The time away could help you build your strength and confidence, overcome your fears and accomplish things you never dreamed you could!

🖊 FILL IN THE GAP

Read the sentences and choose the correct word or words to fill the gap. Refer back to *Residential activities* to find the correct answer.

Using maps, you will need to find various points and record _____.

Working as a team, you use your _____ and balance to stack plastic crates – but you must be stood on top of the crates while you stack!

You hook into the _____ and away you go, zipping through the air from one platform to the next.

....

🔗 MATCHING

Draw a line with a ruler to match the information.

targets at a distance	zip lines
balance, rhythm and determination	archery
requires a harness	kayaking
combines fitness and fun	orienteering

....

🏷 LABEL

Label the description with the correct information.

teaches you how to survive in the wild	
requires coordination and balance	
uses a one-person boat or oar	
involves being guided through an assault course	
uses a compass and a map	
involves hanging from a rope	

....

✓ TRUE OR FALSE

Read the sentences. Put a tick in the correct box to show which sentences are *true* and which are *false*.

Residential activities are ones that don't normally happen at home.　　True ☐　False ☐

Residentials could help you build confidence and overcome your fears.　　True ☐　False ☐

Abseiling requires a boat and an oar.　　True ☐　False ☐

You can practise balance, rhythm and determination through kayaking.　　True ☐　False ☐

Zip lines will teach you how to survive in the wild.　　True ☐　False ☐

　　　　　　　　　　　　　　　　　　　Comprehension Ninja 9–10 © Andrew Jennings, 2020

◎ MULTIPLE CHOICE

Circle the correct answer to the following question.

What fun rating does kayaking have?

| two stars | three stars | four stars | five stars |

123 SEQUENCING

Look at *Residential activities*. Number the statements from 1 to 4 to show the order they occur in the text.

The experience may be the first time children spend a prolonged period of time away from their homes and families, and can form some of the most memorable and rewarding times of their lives.	
The time away could help you build your strength and confidence, overcome your fears and accomplish things you never dreamed you could!	
The first to gather the symbols and return to the beginning wins.	
Use this handy fact file to choose which ones would suit you!	

🔍 FIND AND COPY

These questions are about *Residential activities*.

Look at the 'Zip lines' section. Find and copy a phrase that suggests that the zip line is very exciting and can cause your heart to beat faster.

_____

Look at the 'Crate climbing' section. Find and copy a word that suggests that some boxes will fall over dramatically.

_____

🕯 UNDERLINE OR HIGHLIGHT

Read the paragraph below and then follow the instructions.

Forest adventure

The forest adventure will test all the new skills and knowledge you have gained. Dropped at an unknown point in the forest, you have to use bushcraft and navigation skills to find your way back to base. Can your team return safely?

Underline or highlight a word that means get more or increase a level of something.

Underline or highlight a word that means to decide where to go to arrive somewhere specific.

Icebergs can be as tall as mountains, or disintegrate into little 'bergy bits'. Whatever shape and size they take, these snowy floats form a fascinating part of Earth's oceans.

What is an iceberg?

Icebergs are large pieces of ice that break off from glaciers and other ice structures, which form when falling snow builds up and compacts into ice. These are made of frozen freshwater, not saltwater. When some of this ice breaks away from the structure, an iceberg is created and drifts away to sea – a process known as 'calving'. Although icebergs are extremely heavy, they float in the water as ice is less dense than water.

Icebergs are generally found in the frozen waters near to the North or South Pole. In the northern hemisphere, the majority of icebergs break off from glaciers in Greenland, but can also come from those in Alaska. In the Southern Hemisphere, nearly all icebergs calve from the continent of Antarctica. It is possible, however, for the bergs to drift.

How big is an iceberg?

Icebergs can vary hugely in size. While some are the size of an island, others are tiny in comparison. To be officially classified as an iceberg, the structure must cover an area of at least 500 square metres. Smaller pieces of ice, however, can also be found. 'Bergy bits' are around the size of houses and 'growlers' are similar in size to small cars.

Icebergs are also classified by shape – most frequently as either 'tabular' or 'non-tabular'. A tabular iceberg is a flat-topped iceberg that's usually formed of ice rather than compacted snow and that has broken off an ice sheet or ice shelf. Non-tabular icebergs have different shapes, including domes and spires.

Even when an iceberg doesn't appear to be huge, its appearance can be misleading. Often, as little as an eighth of the iceberg can be seen above the water: below the surface could lie an enormous mass that's hidden from sight. The common expression 'the tip of the iceberg' is linked to this idea: it's used when only part of a situation is known.

Are icebergs dangerous?

Icebergs can be treacherous for ships. Hidden ice can rip holes in them, often too big to repair. A particularly dangerous area of the ocean can be found in the North Atlantic Ocean to the east and south-east of Newfoundland, Canada. It's an area often referred to as Iceberg Alley.

Perhaps the most famous example of an iceberg causing a major catastrophe was the sinking of the Titanic in 1912. The grand and extravagant ship was on its maiden voyage from Southampton to New York carrying over 2,000 passengers. It struck an iceberg that tore a hole in its side. Within hours it had sunk, resulting in the deaths of more than 1,500 people. Shortly after this disaster, an International Ice Patrol was established to track icebergs and warn ships. We can now monitor the movement of icebergs and help avoid future tragedies.

What happens to an iceberg?

Icebergs can drift for thousands of miles. If they travel into warmer waters, they will ultimately melt. When this happens, warm air creates water from the snow and ice on the iceberg's surface, and the pools trickle through the iceberg, causing cracks to appear. At the same time, warmer water causes the iceberg's edges to melt away, and ice to break off.

Despite this, scientists believe that the lifespan of an iceberg – from the first snowfall on a glacier to its melting in the ocean – can be as long as 3,000 years.

⚡ FILL IN THE GAP

Read the sentences and choose the correct word or words to fill the gap. Refer back to *Icebergs* to find the correct answer.

In the northern hemisphere, the majority of icebergs break off from _____ in Greenland, but can also come from those in Alaska.

Perhaps the most famous example of an iceberg causing a major _____ was the sinking of the Titanic in 1912.

When this happens, warm air creates water from the snow and ice on the iceberg's surface, and the pools _____ through the iceberg, causing cracks to appear.

....

🔗 MATCHING

Draw a line with a ruler to match the information.

iceberg creation process	growlers
icebergs the size of cars	'tabular' or 'non-tabular'
icebergs the size of houses	bergy bits
the shape of an iceberg	calving

....

✏️ LABEL

Label the description with the correct information.

icebergs can be treacherous for	
name of flat-topped iceberg usually formed of ice	
dome and spire shaped icebergs	
icebergs break off from	
type of water that icebergs are made from	
the North Atlantic Ocean near Canada is often referred to as	

....

✓ TRUE OR FALSE

Read the sentences. Put a tick in the correct box to show which sentences are *true* and which are *false*.

'The bottom of the iceberg' is a common expression.   True ☐   False ☐

Icebergs normally melt after around ten miles of drifting.   True ☐   False ☐

It can take up to 3,000 years for an iceberg to melt.   True ☐   False ☐

The south-east of Newfoundland, Canada is a particularly dangerous part of the ocean.   True ☐   False ☐

All 2,000 people aboard the Titanic drowned.   True ☐   False ☐

◎ MULTIPLE CHOICE

Circle the correct answer to the following question.

The Titanic departed from Southampton. Where was its destination?

| Newfoundland | Alaska | Canada | New York |

123 SEQUENCING

Look at *Icebergs*. Number the statements from 1 to 4 to show the order they occur in the text.

To be officially classified as an iceberg, the structure must cover an area of at least 500 square metres.	
Although icebergs are extremely heavy, they float in the water as ice is less dense than water.	
Shortly after this disaster, an International Ice Patrol was established to track icebergs and warn ships.	
Icebergs can be treacherous for ships.	

🔍 FIND AND COPY

These questions are about *Icebergs*.

Look at the paragraph beginning 'Perhaps the most famous example…'. Find and copy a word that suggests that there was an unexpected event that caused huge loss.

_____

Look at the paragraph beginning 'Even when an iceberg…'. Find and copy a word that suggests that people might not realise how big icebergs were.

_____

◑ UNDERLINE OR HIGHLIGHT

Read the paragraph below and then follow the instructions.

The grand and extravagant ship was on its maiden voyage from Southampton to New York carrying over 2,000 passengers. It struck an iceberg that tore a hole in its side. Within hours it had sunk, resulting in the deaths of more than 1,500 people. Shortly after this disaster, an International Ice Patrol was established to track icebergs and warn ships. We can now monitor the movement of icebergs and help avoid future tragedies.

Underline or highlight a word that means elaborate and impressive.

Underline or highlight a word that means to prevent from happening again.

Rainforests are Earth's oldest ecosystems. They are vast areas of land dense with tall trees that receive regular downpours of rain. Rainforests are found in hot climates near the Equator, like the Amazon rainforest found in South America. The perfect combination of heavy rainfall, plentiful sunlight and nutrient-rich soil allows thousands of trees and plants to grow and provides perfect habitats for some of our planet's most enchanting animals.

These are just some of the creatures that live in the Amazon rainforest, and just some of the fascinating facts about them.

Sloth (Scientific name: *Folivora*)

Sloths are mammals famous for their slowness and relaxed nature. They spend most of their days in trees, eating or hanging upside down. Sloths are much safer in trees: on the ground, they are clumsy – and would be easy targets for ground predators, which are animals that want to eat them, such as leopards and snakes. Interestingly, though, they are excellent swimmers.

A sloth has little reason to leave the trees as their diet mostly consists of leaves. They are also camouflaged there: they can blend into their rainforest surroundings because they move so slowly that green algae grows on their fur!

Harpy eagle (Scientific name: *Harpia harpyja*)

The harpy eagle is an apex predator in the rainforest. Apex predators exist at the top of the food chain: they have no natural predators themselves. The health of a rainforest and its ecosystem can often be gauged by a healthy presence of apex predators, as there must be plentiful species in the forest to feed them. Sloths, monkeys and some rodents are often harpy eagles' main targets for food.

These eagles have shorter wingspans than other eagles, which allows them to manoeuvre through the thickly forested surroundings.

The species is currently listed as 'near threatened'; it is estimated that there are only between 20,000 and 50,000 birds now living in the wild.

 Comprehension Ninja 9–10 © Andrew Jennings, 2020

Piranha (Scientific name: *Pygocentrus nattereri*)

Piranhas are fish famous for being vicious predators. They attack ferociously in groups and can devour large animals, including human beings, in seconds. However, the piranha is actually an omnivore, which means that it eats both plants and animals. A piranha's diet is a mixture of insects, fish, snails, worms and various plants. The only time these fish will dine on a large mammal is if a dead one falls into the water.

Piranhas are found in freshwater lakes and rivers, and generally live in packs – but not for the reason you may think. Many people think that pack behaviour is a hunting technique. It is actually a self-defence technique, designed to protect the fish from other predators, such as crocodiles, turtles and birds.

Emerald tree boa (Scientific name: *Corallus caninus*)

Considering this beautiful reptile is called an emerald (green) tree snake, it's surprising that they are actually born brick-red, bright red or even yellow in colour: they turn green only after a year. Their primary foods include lizards; birds; rats, bats and similar rodents; and also larger mammals such as possums. Emerald tree boas are found in the rainforests of northern South America. They are solitary and they spend their lives in the branches of trees, only descending to the ground to move between them.

Endangered animals

Many animals that live in rainforests around the world are endangered: they are close to extinction, which means there will be no more of the animal left in the world.

Bengal tigers, jaguars, leopards; golden lion tamarin monkeys, chimpanzees, orang-utans and gorillas; poison dart frogs; manatees; toucans – all of these species are endangered, and it's largely because their rainforest habitats are being destroyed for development, logging and agriculture.

Drastic action must be taken to protect them.

✒ FILL IN THE GAP

Read the sentences and choose the correct word or words to fill the gap. Refer back to *Rainforest animals* to find the correct answer.

The perfect combination of heavy rainfall, plentiful sunlight and _____ soil allows thousands of trees and plants to grow and provides perfect habitats for some of our planet's most enchanting animals.

The health of a rainforest and its ecosystem can often be gauged by a healthy presence of _____, as there must be plentiful species in the forest to feed them.

_____ are found in freshwater lakes and rivers, and generally live in packs – but not for the reason you may think.

✚ MATCHING

Draw a line with a ruler to match the information.

harpy eagle		*Folivora*
emerald tree boa		*Harpia harpyja*
sloth		*Corallus caninus*
piranha		*Pygocentrus nattereri*

✐ LABEL

Label the description with the correct animal.

sloths, monkeys and rodents are its main target for food	
find life safer in trees	
found in freshwater lakes and rivers	
solitary and spend lives in the branches of trees	
some are born a brick-red colour	
listed as a 'near threatened' species	

✔ TRUE OR FALSE

Read the sentences. Put a tick in the correct box to show which sentences are *true* and which are *false*.

Harpy eagles have longer wingspans than other eagles.　　　True ☐　False ☐

Sloths can devour large animals including human beings.　　　True ☐　False ☐

Many animals that live in rainforests around the world are endangered.　　　True ☐　False ☐

Green algae grows on the harpy eagle.　　　True ☐　False ☐

The piranha is an omnivore.　　　True ☐　False ☐

◎ MULTIPLE CHOICE

Circle the correct answer to the following question.

Which animal is camouflaged so they can blend into their rainforest surroundings?

harpy eagle	sloth	piranha	emerald tree boa

123 SEQUENCING

Look at *Rainforest animals*. Number the statements from 1 to 4 to show the order they occur in the text.

Apex predators exist at the top of the food chain: they have no natural predators themselves.	
They attack ferociously in groups, and can devour large animals, including human beings, in seconds.	
They spend most of their days in trees, eating or hanging upside down.	
Their primary foods include lizards; birds; rats, bats and similar rodents; and also larger mammals such as possums.	

🔍 FIND AND COPY

These questions are about *Rainforest animals*.

Look at the 'Emerald tree boa' section. Find and copy a word that suggests that this animal lives on its own.

_____

Look at the 'Endangered animals' section. Find and copy a word that suggests that the action needed to protect animals is extreme.

_____

✋ UNDERLINE OR HIGHLIGHT

Read the paragraph below and then follow the instructions.

> The harpy eagle is an apex predator in the rainforest. Apex predators exist at the top of the food chain: they have no natural predators themselves. The health of a rainforest and its ecosystem can often be gauged by a healthy presence of apex predators, as there must be plentiful species in the forest to feed them. Sloths, monkeys and some rodents are often harpy eagles' main targets for food.

Underline or highlight a word that means to exist in large numbers.

Underline or highlight a word that means something can be calculated or measured.

What is gravity?

Gravity is an invisible force that pulls one thing towards another. We usually discuss it in relation to planets: it is the force that means a planet pulls objects towards its centre. Gravity holds Earth and the other planets in our Solar System, around the Sun.

The gravitational pull of an object depends on its mass and how close it is to the other object. Anything that has mass also has a gravitational pull.

What is mass?

Mass is the amount of matter something contains. A greater mass means that the matter is more closely packed together. On Earth, we can measure mass using weight: weight measures how strongly an object's mass is being pulled towards Earth by gravity. The greater the mass is, the more strongly it is pulled.

Gravity on Earth comes from Earth's mass. If someone were on a planet with less mass than Earth, they would weigh less than they do on our planet. If the planet's mass was larger, they would weigh more.

What does gravity do?

Gravity is extremely important on Earth. It keeps us at a comfortable distance from the Sun, which means that we can use its light and warmth to live. It also holds the Moon near to Earth.

The gravitational pull of the Moon pulls Earth's seas towards it, causing tides at different times of the day – but Earth's gravitational pull on the seas is stronger than the Moon's, so they don't fly off into space! Gravity is also what keeps us on the ground and causes things to fall.

Who discovered gravity?

People have been aware that a force is keeping us on the ground for thousands of years. Aristotle, an Ancient Greek philosopher who lived 384–322 BCE, suggested that objects fell at a speed decided by their weight. He believed that the heavier an object was, the quicker it would fall to the ground.

The man credited with discovering gravity, however, was English scientist Sir Isaac Newton. Two thousand years after Aristotle, in the 1600s, Newton is said to have developed his theory of gravity while sitting under a tree. A story tells of how he was struck on the head by a falling apple. He began to question why such objects would fall to the ground, not sideways or upwards. Newton also became interested in how the Moon moves in relation to the Earth – and began to establish a link.

Newton described gravity, accurately, as a 'drawing power' and said that 'the sum of the drawing power must be in the Earth's centre, not in any side of the Earth.'

In 1687, he published his discoveries about gravity in his famous book, *Philosophiæ Naturalis Principia Mathematica* ('Mathematical Principles of Natural Philosophy'). His findings are known today as Newton's Law of Universal Attraction.

Newton died in 1727, but his legacy and work live on. All forces are now measured in Newtons (N) using a Newton-metre. The apple tree that is said to have inspired his ideas can also still be found at his old home, which is now owned by the National Trust and has many visitors from around the world. Our understanding of gravity is just one breakthrough in physics, which helps us to understand the things that happen around us every day.

✏️ FILL IN THE GAP

Read the sentences and choose the correct word or words to fill the gap. Refer back to *Gravity* to find the correct answer.

We usually discuss it in relation to _____: it is the force that means a planet pulls objects towards its centre.

Newton also became interested in how the _____ moves in relation to the Earth – and began to establish a link.

The _____ that is said to have inspired his ideas can also still be found at his old home, which is now owned by the National Trust and has many visitors from around the world.

....

🔗 MATCHING

Draw a line with a ruler to match the information.

ancient Greek philosopher	•	•	Newton
an invisible force	•	•	Aristotle
discovered gravity	•	•	gravity
famous book	•	•	*Philosophiæ Naturalis Principia Mathematica*

....

✏️ LABEL

Label the description with the correct information.

helps keep human beings on the ground	
pulls the Earth's seas away from the Earth	
Aristotle suggested that objects falling speed depends on	
Newton was struck on the head by an	
Newton's old home is owned by	
all forces are now measured using a	

....

✅ TRUE OR FALSE

Read the sentences. Put a tick in the correct box to show which sentences are *true* and which are *false*.

Newton's apple tree is now owned by the National Trust.　　True ☐　False ☐

Aristotle was credited with discovering gravity.　　True ☐　False ☐

The Moon prevents the oceans flying into space.　　True ☐　False ☐

Newton's findings are known today as Newton's Law of Universal Attraction.　　True ☐　False ☐

We can measure mass using weight.　　True ☐　False ☐

◎ MULTIPLE CHOICE

Circle the correct answer to the following question.

When did Aristotle live?

384–322 BCE	385–322 BCE	348–323 BCE	389–333 BCE

123 SEQUENCING

Look at *Gravity*. Number the statements from 1 to 4 to show the order they occur in the text.

On Earth, we can measure mass using weight: weight measures how strongly an object's mass is being pulled towards Earth by gravity.	
Two thousand years after Aristotle, in the 1600s, Newton is said to have developed his theory of gravity while sitting under a tree.	
Gravity is an invisible force that pulls one thing towards another.	
Gravity is extremely important on Earth.	

🔎 FIND AND COPY

These questions are about *Gravity*.

Look at the 'What does gravity do?' section. Find and copy a word that suggests the Earth is the perfect distance from the Sun, so that we are in no direct danger or problems.

_____

Look at the 'Who discovered gravity?' section. Find and copy a word that suggests that Newton's work still impacts us today.

_____

◖ UNDERLINE OR HIGHLIGHT

Read the paragraph below and then follow the instructions.

Gravity is an invisible force that pulls one thing towards another. We usually discuss it in relation to planets: it is the force that means a planet pulls objects towards its centre. Gravity holds Earth and the other planets in our Solar System, around the Sun.

Underline or highlight a word that means something can't be seen.

Underline or highlight a word that means to talk about.

Kangaroos, beaches, barbecues – there are lots of stereotyped images associated with Australia! There's a lot more you may not know about Australia, though: its geography, people and culture.

Australia is the sixth largest country in the world. It's home to more than 20 million people, and has a varied and fascinating culture.

Geography

The climates in Australia are diverse. More than a third of the country is hot desert – this wide, almost unpopulated space is called the 'outback'. Here, temperatures can be extremely high and there is little water or vegetation. Towards the country's south, though, the climate is more accommodating and the land is fertile. There you will find most Australian cities and farms.

Contrary to popular belief, Sydney is not the capital city of Australia – although it does attract the majority of visitors due to its tourist attractions, including its iconic Opera House. Canberra, with a population of nearly 400,000, is the country's capital.

Visitors to Australia also marvel at many of the country's natural features. Uluru (also known as Ayers Rock) is one of its most impressive landmarks. This sacred natural formation stands at around 350 metres tall. It can be found in the Uluru-Kata Tjuta National Park, in the centre of the country and the outback.

Perhaps the most impressive natural wonder, however, is the Great Barrier Reef. This reef – the largest coral reef in the world – is larger than the Great Wall of China. It comprises over 3,000 individual reef systems. Visitors can scuba dive or snorkel to find an abundance of marvellous marine life.

Inhabitants

Australia is home to around 25 million people – five times more than its neighbour, New Zealand. The most populated city in the country is Sydney, which is home to over 4.5 million people. Melbourne follows closely behind: it's home to more than 4 million residents, making even this city ten times bigger than Canberra.

Australia is also home to a diverse range of animals. Due to its remote location, a number of them are not found elsewhere, koalas, kangaroos and platypuses among them. This may be a good thing though, as some of the most dangerous creatures in the world live there too: 36 species of poisonous funnel-web spiders, and 20 different kinds of venomous snakes.

History

Australia's Aboriginal people are believed to have populated the country for at least 50,000 years. They lived in hundreds of different clans, each with a spiritual connection to their land.

Dutch explorers landed in Australia in 1606 and then, in 1770, a British explorer named Captain James Cook claimed Australia for Britain. Colonies and farms were built, but conditions were harsh. Seventeen years later, Britain decided to populate Australia by sending convicted British criminals to serve their sentences there. These new arrivals on the island destroyed the lives of many Aboriginal people, stealing their land and uprooting their lifestyles.

Over the years, soldiers, officers and freed convicts began to build more farms in Australia. More people later moved there in search of cheap land and new opportunities. When gold was found in New South Wales and Victoria, thousands of hopeful people from around the world headed to the island in search of riches. Many of them decided not to return to their homelands and settled in Australia.

In 1901, Australia's six states became a single nation. Despite this, Australia retains diverse cultures, peoples, religions and languages. It is thought that people originally from more than 200 countries call Australia home, and that over 300 languages are spoken. Nearly a quarter of all those living in Australia were born in other countries.

✏️ FILL IN THE GAP

Read the sentences and choose the correct word or words to fill the gap. Refer back to *Australia* to find the correct answer.

Contrary to popular belief, _____ is not the capital city of Australia – although it does attract the majority of visitors due to its tourist attractions, including its iconic Opera House.

_____ follows closely behind: it's home to more than 4 million residents, making even this city ten times bigger than Canberra.

When gold was found in _____ and Victoria, thousands of hopeful people from around the world headed to the island in search of riches.

....

➕ MATCHING

Draw a line with a ruler to match the information.

koalas, kangaroos and platypuses ●	● geography
Dutch explorers landed in 1606 ●	● inhabitants
Uluru ●	● history
beaches and barbecues ●	● Australian stereotypes

....

🏷️ LABEL

Label the description with the correct information.

the largest coral reef in the world	
the year Australia's six states became one	
number of species of poisonous funnel-web spider	
ten times bigger than Canberra	
the capital city of Australia	
metal found in New South Wales and Victoria	

....

✔️ TRUE OR FALSE

Read the sentences. Put a tick in the correct box to show which sentences are *true* and which are *false*.

Sentence	True	False
Over 300 languages are spoken in Australia.	☐	☐
Captain James Cook claimed Australia for the Dutch in 1606.	☐	☐
Aboriginal people have inhabited Australia for at least 50,000 years.	☐	☐
Australia is the fifth largest country in the world.	☐	☐
More than a third of the country is hot desert.	☐	☐

◎ MULTIPLE CHOICE

Circle the correct answer to the following question.

What is the capital city of Australia?

Canberra	Sydney	Melbourne	New South Wales

123 SEQUENCING

Look at *Australia*. Number the statements from 1 to 4 to show the order they occur in the text.

It can be found in the Uluru-Kata Tjuta National Park, in the centre of the country and the outback.	
It's home to more than 20 million people, and has a varied and fascinating culture.	
This may be a good thing though, as some of the most dangerous creatures in the world live there too: 36 species of poisonous funnel-web spiders, and 20 different kinds of venomous snakes.	
The most populated city in the country is Sydney, which is home to over 4.5 million people.	

🔎 FIND AND COPY

These questions are about *Australia*.

Look at the 'Inhabitants' section. Find and copy a word that suggests that a large number of human beings live in Sydney.

_____

Look at the 'History' section. Find and copy a word that suggests that people decided to live in Australia rather than returning home.

_____

🌑 UNDERLINE OR HIGHLIGHT

Read the paragraph below and then follow the instructions.

> Australia is also home to a diverse range of animals. Due to its remote location, a number of them are not found elsewhere, koalas, kangaroos and platypuses among them. This may be a good thing, though, as some of the most dangerous creatures in the world live there, too: 36 species of poisonous funnel-web spiders, and 20 different kinds of venomous snakes.

Underline or highlight a word that means made up of a wide variety.

Underline or highlight a word that means far away and difficult to get to.

20 MOSQUES

Mosques are Muslim places of worship. The Arabic word for mosque, masjid, means 'place of prostration' – a place for bowing down. Anywhere Muslims pray can be called a mosque, whether it's a building or in the open air.

Mosque buildings are sacred to Islam, and can be found all over the world. In the United Kingdom, there are around 3 million Muslims – around 5 per cent of the population – and there are around 1,750 mosques.

Mosques are places for Muslims to meet for prayers, to study and to respect festivals such as Ramadan and Eid. They are important for funerals and marriage ceremonies, and for making honourable business agreements. Some mosques are also used as homeless shelters, community centres and schools.

The first ever mosque was the Prophet Mohammed's home in Medina, Saudi Arabia, a 7th-century house with a large courtyard surrounded by long rooms. The biggest mosque in the world is the Al Haram Mosque in Mecca, Saudi Arabia. Muslims attempt to journey to this holy place at least once in their lives. It can accommodate an astonishing 4 million people at once. The Al Haram surrounds the Ka'aba, a cuboid-shaped building that is the holiest place in Islam. This is home to the Black Stone, which was set into the Ka'aba's walls by the Prophet Mohammed before his first revelation. Regardless of where Muslims are in the world, when they pray, they pray towards Mecca.

Although some mosques are private places, others welcome thousands of visitors each year. Suitable clothing is required: it must not show too much skin. Long trousers and shirts or t-shirts are suitable for men, while women must also cover their arms, heads and necks.

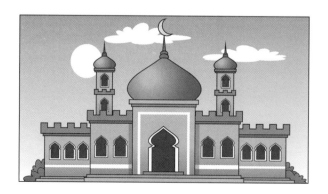

One of the first things that a visitor to a mosque encounters is a shoe rack. Worshippers and visitors are expected to remove their shoes as they enter the mosque, to prevent dirt from entering the holy space. Before Muslims pray, they must also perform a ritual washing (wudu). This is done in the ablutions area. While some bigger mosques have fountains in their entrances and courtyards, worshippers may use bathrooms in smaller mosques. Washing before prayer symbolises spiritual cleansing and a spirit of purity before coming before the Muslim God, Allah Almighty.

The biggest spaces in mosques are their prayer halls, also known as musallas. They do not have seats: worshippers instead use prayer mats. These spaces were designed to allow the entire male population of a city or town to sit on the floor and pray. Women are allowed to attend the hall on Fridays, but traditionally are separated from men and pray in separate areas.

Another important part of the mosque is the mihrab. This semi-circular hollow in the wall indicates the direction of Mecca, allowing Muslims to pray in its direction. Next to the mihrab is the minbar, from where sermons are delivered.

Mosques can have symbolic traditional features. As it is disrespectful to create images and pictures of the Islamic God and prophets, they are decorated with patterns and stained glass. They also feature tall towers called 'minarets', which means 'lighthouses' in Arabic. Before the five daily prayers, a Muslim crier stands at the top of a minaret, calling worshippers to prayer. A dome, or qubba, is traditionally found on top of a mosque, above the large prayer hall. Although on early mosques the dome would take up only part of the roof, bigger domes can be the size of the entire roof of the prayer hall. The dome is a symbol of the sky and 'Jannah', the paradise Muslims believe awaits them after death.

✏️ FILL IN THE GAP

Read the sentences and choose the correct word or words to fill the gap. Refer back to _Mosques_ to find the correct answer.

The first ever mosque was the Prophet Mohammed's home in _____, Saudi Arabia, a 7th-century house with a large courtyard surrounded by long rooms.

While some bigger mosques have _____ in their entrances and courtyards, worshippers may use bathrooms in smaller mosques.

As it is _____ to create images and pictures of the Islamic God and prophets, they are decorated with patterns and stained glass.

🔗 MATCHING

Draw a line with a ruler to match the information.

festival		Ramadan
holiest place in Islam		minarets
Medina		Ka'aba
tall towers on mosques		Prophet Mohammed

🏷️ LABEL

Label the description with the correct information.

the biggest space in a mosque	
one of the first things encountered in a mosque	
ritual performed before praying	
mosque prayer halls have no	
a semi-circular hollow in the wall	
traditionally found on top of a mosque	

✔️ TRUE OR FALSE

Read the sentences. Put a tick in the correct box to show which sentences are _true_ and which are _false_.

	True	False
Minaret means lighthouse in Arabic.	☐	☐
Sermons are delivered from the mihrab.	☐	☐
Muslims pray towards Mecca.	☐	☐
The dome on top of a mosque is a symbol of the sky and paradise.	☐	☐
Some mosques welcome thousands of visitors each year.	☐	☐

◎ MULTIPLE CHOICE

Circle the correct answer to the following question.

What percentage of the UK population is Muslim?

5 per cent	15 per cent	25 per cent	50 per cent

123 SEQUENCING

Look at *Mosques*. Number the statements from 1 to 4 to show the order they occur in the text.

Mosque buildings are sacred to Islam, and can be found all over the world.	
The Al Haram surrounds the Ka'aba, a cuboid-shaped building that is the holiest place in Islam.	
Long trousers and shirts or t-shirts are suitable for men, while women must also cover their arms, heads and necks.	
Women are allowed to attend the hall on Fridays, but traditionally are separated from men and pray in separate areas.	

🔎 FIND AND COPY

These questions are about *Mosques*.

Look at the paragraph beginning 'One of the first things'. Find and copy a word that suggests that worshippers want to stop or not allow something to happen.

_____

Look at the paragraph beginning 'The first ever mosque'. Find and copy a word that suggests it can hold or has the space for lots of people to be there at once.

_____

🌑 UNDERLINE OR HIGHLIGHT

Read the paragraph below and then follow the instructions.

A dome, or qubba, is traditionally found on top of a mosque, above the large prayer hall. Although on early mosques the dome would take up only part of the roof, bigger domes can be the size of the entire roof of the prayer hall. The dome is a symbol of the sky and 'Jannah', the paradise Muslims believe awaits them after death.

Underline or highlight a word that means a custom or belief has happened for a long time.

Underline or highlight a word that means a wonderful place where people go when they die.

21 WOLVES

Like human beings, wolves are extremely sociable animals. They live in groups known as packs. Pack sizes vary, but commonly contain six to seven wolves – although some can be much larger, containing up to 15. Most packs contain two adult wolves, a male and a female, and their offspring. The adult male is the leader of the pack, known as the 'alpha' male. The word 'alpha' is used because it is the first letter of the ancient Greek alphabet; it names a wolf as the first most important male. Alphas make all of the decisions for the pack, such where they go and when they hunt.

Wolf communication

Again like humans, wolves use sounds, facial expressions and body language to communicate with each other. Alphas show their control of other wolves by glaring at them directly in the eyes – other wolves won't make direct eye contact with the alpha unless he initiates it. When the alpha is showing his authority, other wolves will submit by lowering their heads and then bodies to bow down. They may also press their noses up against the alpha to show their respect.

Wolves' reputation

Wolves have featured in children's and adults' literature for centuries, often being portrayed as the enemy or 'bad guy'. Children are taught to consider wolves this way in the first stories they're likely to hear. In Little Red Riding Hood, the wolf is a cunning man-eater who's dead set on devouring the girl. In The Three Little Pigs, he's yet again a trickster with a vicious plan, trying to convince the pigs to trust him. Of course, wolves were a very real threat at the time these tales were written. Many later stories for older children and adults, though, appreciate the natural majesty of the animals. The novel *White Fang* is written mostly from a wolf's point of view, and explores the violence of the human world as well as of the natural world.

Comprehension Ninja 9–10 © Andrew Jennings, 2020

Wolves' environmental effects

In 1995, the grey wolf was reintroduced to the Yellowstone National Park in America, after having been killed off in the 1930s. The effect of the wolves returning to the park has been staggering. Beforehand, animal species of many kinds were dwindling and trees were dying: the ecosystem wasn't balanced. With the wolves back at the top of the food chain, everything changed. Trees recovered and grew stronger as the wolves forced elks to move around the park, rather than destroying the trees by grazing in one area. As a result of the trees growing, many bird and insect species returned to Yellowstone, as they now had a sustainable habitat. Beaver colonies also flourished, increasing from only one to nine. As the beavers built dams, water levels were stabilised and fish stocks grew.

Wolves of the world

Grey wolves are also known as common wolves. Most familiar images of wolves – certainly most illustrations of them – show grey wolves.

Arctic wolves have unique colouring, with thick white fur. This allows them to blend in with the Arctic snow.

Red wolves get their name from their appearance – their colouring is like foxes'. Red wolves are believed to be descended from coyotes as well as wolves.

Indian wolves, unsurprisingly, live mostly in Asia. Their populations are relatively high, as Hindus consider killing wolves to be extremely bad luck.

Himalayan wolves are a sub-species of grey wolves, identified as different only recently. As their name suggests, most Himalayan wolves live in the mountains.

Ethiopian wolves are also called 'Simien jackals' because of their jackal-like appearance. They are Africa's rarest carnivores – even more endangered than gorillas.

⏱ FILL IN THE GAP

Read the sentences and choose the correct word or words to fill the gap. Refer back to *Wolves* to find the correct answer.

Alphas show their control of other wolves by glaring at them directly in the eyes – other wolves won't make direct eye contact with the _____ unless he initiates it.

With the _____ back at the top of the food chain, everything changed.

Their populations are relatively high, as Hindus consider _____ wolves to be extremely bad luck.

🔗 MATCHING

Draw a line with a ruler to match the information.

Yellowstone National Park	•	•	alpha wolf
no eye contact	•	•	bad-guy wolf
literature	•	•	Indian wolf
live mostly in Asia	•	•	reintroduced grey wolves

🏷 LABEL

Label the description with the correct information.

bad luck to kill these wolves	
coloured like foxes	
sub-species of the grey wolf	
unique thick white fur	
Africa's rarest carnivore	
the most common type of wolf	

⚡ TRUE OR FALSE

Read the sentences. Put a tick in the correct box to show which sentences are *true* and which are *false*.

Eye contact with the alpha is seen as a mark of respect to authority.   True ☐   False ☐

Wolves are often seen positively in literature.   True ☐   False ☐

Red wolves are named because of their association with Little Red Riding Hood.   True ☐   False ☐

Wolves were a very real threat in the past.   True ☐   False ☐

The novel *White Fang* explores the violence of the human world.   True ☐   False ☐

◎ MULTIPLE CHOICE

Circle the correct answer to the following question.

Which is the most common type of wolf?

| red wolf | Ethiopian wolf | Indian wolf | grey wolf |

123 SEQUENCING

Look at *Wolves*. Number the statements from 1 to 4 to show the order they occur in the text.

Himalayan wolves are a sub-species of grey wolves, identified as different only recently.	
Indian wolves, unsurprisingly, live mostly in Asia.	
Red wolves get their name from their appearance – their colouring is like foxes'.	
Arctic wolves have unique colouring, with thick white fur.	

🔍 FIND AND COPY

These questions are about *Wolves*.

Look at the paragraph beginning 'In 1995'. Find and copy a word that suggests wolves came back to Yellowstone.

_____

Look at the paragraph beginning 'In 1995'. Find and copy a word that suggests that many animal species were reducing in number.

_____

🌓 UNDERLINE OR HIGHLIGHT

Read the paragraph below and then follow the instructions.

Wolves have featured in children's and adults' literature for centuries, often being portrayed at the enemy or 'bad guy'. Children are taught to consider wolves this way in the first stories they're likely to hear. In Little Red Riding Hood, the wolf is a cunning man-eater who's dead set on devouring the girl. In The Three Little Pigs, he's yet again a trickster with a vicious plan, trying to convince the pigs to trust him.

Underline or highlight a word that means hundreds of years.

Underline or highlight a word that means to achieve what you want by cleverly deceiving or tricking others.

22 GERMS: UNWANTED INVADERS

Germs are the invaders of the body. They could be bacteria, viruses, fungus or one of many other disease-causing enemies. They can by spread in blood, sweat or saliva – especially in coughs and sneezes, which shoot the germs into the air. A single sneeze can expel 40,000 particles into the air, at around 50 miles per hour, which can travel as far as 30 feet!

You may then breathe the germs in – but you don't have to be present to catch the germs in a cough or sneeze. Germs can live outside of people: you could pick them up by simply putting your hand on a nearby surface afterwards. After that, you could spread them to everywhere else you touch. When you eat, you'll also transfer the germs to your food and eat them.

Once they're inside your body, the germs begin to multiply. They attack the cells in the body, damaging them, killing them or producing toxic chemicals.

The body's defences

There are lots of parts of your body that you can't see with your own eyes. One of these is the 'immune system', which is what we call the body's defence system. Your immune system defends your body from illnesses with its very own army of soldiers: white blood cells. White blood cells, and the chemicals they make, attack and kill cells they don't recognise. Unfortunately, white blood cells can't always defeat these unwanted invaders.

Vaccines

Some illnesses can be extremely serious – even fatal. In the past, many diseases that are minor or rare today, such as chicken pox and measles, killed thousands of people. Many are no longer deadly because of vaccines. Vaccines are weakened or dead samples of germs. They are injected into healthy people, causing their bodies' white blood cells to fight them and win. The white blood cells never forget how to create the chemicals that beat the germs. This means that the body knows how to kill full-strength germs of the same type, and is known as becoming 'immune'. Vaccines have saved millions of lives across the world.

 Comprehension Ninja 9–10 © Andrew Jennings, 2020

Unfortunately, many people aren't educated well enough about the power of vaccines. Some of them don't understand the way they work, and some hear bad things about possible side effects. The risks of the diseases, though, are far higher than the risks of the side effects. Diseases like measles still kill children who haven't had vaccines, all over the world.

Creating a vaccine

Edward Jenner, who lived 1749–1823, was an English doctor who helped create and popularise a vaccination for smallpox. Through his pioneering work, he helped save the lives of countless people. Over time, he became known as the 'father of immunology' and of later vaccinations.

Jenner observed that milkmaids who were in close contact with cows very rarely caught smallpox – although they did catch cowpox, a related virus that was far less dangerous. He developed a theory that giving people a small amount of the cowpox virus could make them immune from smallpox.

In 1796, Jenner tested his theory by infecting James Phipps, a boy of eight, with cowpox blisters from the hand of a milkmaid with the disease. The young James developed a mild fever, but soon recovered. Then Jenner exposed James to a weak form of the smallpox virus. As Jenner had suspected, the boy was completely unaffected by it: he had become immune.

New vaccines are developed every day to try and save human lives. Some diseases, such as whooping cough, diphtheria and meningitis C have been almost eliminated. Others, including smallpox and polio, have been destroyed completely.

✏️ FILL IN THE GAP

Read the sentences and choose the correct word or words to fill the gap. Refer back to
Germs: unwanted invaders **to find the correct answer.**

They can by spread in blood, sweat or _____ – especially in coughs and sneezes,
which shoot the germs into the air.

In the past many diseases that are minor or rare today, such as chicken pox and
_____, killed thousands of people.

Jenner observed that milkmaids who were in close contact with cows very rarely caught
_____ – although they did catch cowpox, a related virus that was far

less dangerous.

🔗 MATCHING

Draw a line with a ruler to match the information.

milkmaids rarely caught
Jenner infected
never forget chemical codes
Edward Jenner

father of immunology
James Phipps
smallpox
white blood cells

🏷️ LABEL

Label the description with the correct information.

father of immunology	
infected with smallpox by Jenner	
often contracted cowpox	
have saved millions of lives across the world	
the body's very own army of soldiers	
invaders of the body	

✅ TRUE OR FALSE

Read the sentences. Put a tick in the correct box to show which sentences are *true* and which are *false*.

Sneezes travel at around 50 miles per hour.	True ☐	False ☐
Germs can produce toxic chemicals in your body.	True ☐	False ☐
Vaccines inject dead germs into your body.	True ☐	False ☐
In the past, chicken pox could be fatal.	True ☐	False ☐
Measles has been destroyed completely.	True ☐	False ☐

◎ MULTIPLE CHOICE

Circle the correct answer to the following question.

What did Edward Jenner infect James Phipps with?

meningitis C	measles	chicken pox	smallpox

....

🔢 SEQUENCING

Look at *Germs: unwanted invaders*. Number the statements from 1 to 4 to show the order they occur in the text.

The white blood cells never forget how to create the chemicals that beat the germs.	
Some diseases, such as whooping cough, diphtheria and meningitis C, have been almost eliminated.	
He developed a theory that giving people a small amount of the cowpox virus could make them immune from smallpox.	
They attack the cells in the body, damaging them, killing them or producing toxic chemicals.	

....

🔍 FIND AND COPY

These questions are about *Germs: unwanted invaders*.

Look at the paragraph beginning 'Jenner observed'. Find and copy a word that suggests that people could no longer become ill with smallpox.

_____

Look at the paragraph beginning 'Some illnesses can be extremely serious'. Find and copy a word that suggests something can cause death.

_____

....

✋ UNDERLINE OR HIGHLIGHT

Read the paragraph below and then follow the instructions.

> In 1796, Jenner tested his theory by infecting James Phipps, a boy of eight, with cowpox blisters from the hand of a milkmaid with the disease. The young James developed a mild fever, but soon recovered. Then Jenner exposed James to a weak form of the smallpox virus. As Jenner had suspected, the boy was completely unaffected by it: he had become immune.

Underline or highlight a word that means thought to or believed to be true based on evidence.

Underline or highlight a word that means not too strong or harsh.

Who is Banksy?

Banksy is a street artist whose identity remains unknown. He rose to prominence in the late 1990s for stencilled pieces of graffiti that are intended make a political or social point.

You may have seen images of Banksy's graffiti art. One of his most famous stencils is 'Girl with Balloon', which shows a young girl letting go of a heart-shaped balloon. Many see it as a reflection of children's loss of innocence and people's lack of respect for love.

Banksy furthered his reputation when he tricked everybody at a London art auction. In 2018, a framed copy of 'Girl with Balloon' was sold for £1 million to an anonymous phone bidder. Seconds afterwards, a mechanism hidden in its frame shredded it! The shredding stopped half way through the image, leaving half of it whole and half in strips. This piece of art was given a new name: 'Love is in the Bin' – and it's believed to be worth at least 50 per cent more now than when it was undamaged.

Art or vandalism?

Despite the prices paid for his work, many people believe Banksy's art is simple criminal damage because graffiti is illegal. Many also suggest that allowing it to remain in public spaces sets a bad example for other graffiti artists. Some simply think that his comments aren't effective.

Banksy facts – or are they?

Some information about Banksy can be worked out from his art and some details have been given in interviews.

1. Banksy was born in Bristol in 1974, and was the son of a photocopier engineer.

2. When he started creating graffiti art, he was part of the DryBreadZ Crew, a Bristol-based gang.

3. At that point, his work was mainly done freehand. It was only in the late 1990s that his use of stencils in his work developed. They allow complex images to be created quickly – which is important when they're a crime!

4. Banksy says his work was inspired by 3D, a member of the band Massive Attack.

5. He is often compared to French masters of street art, Blek le Rat and Jef Aerosol – but some say he stole their ideas.

6. Banksy has compiled a book called *Wall and Piece*. It contains images of his works, and also some of his thoughts and ideas.

7. He paid an odd tribute to Monet's 'Water Lilies' by adding an old shopping trolley and rubbish to the painting.

8. Banksy does not sell his work through commercial art galleries.

9. In 2004, he printed spoof £10 notes. The Queen was replaced by Princess Diana's face and they said 'Banksy of England' instead of 'Bank of England'.

10. In 2007, Banksy won the 'Greatest Living Briton – The Arts' prize. Naturally, he didn't collect the prize in person.

People have used these clues to come up with theories about who Banksy really is. The person most commonly believed to be Banksy is Robin Gunningham, an artist who was born in Bristol in 1973. Pictures never show Banksy's face but some contain other details that people believe resemble him. Gunningham also moved to London around 2000, which is when Banksy's artwork started appearing there.

Some of Banksy's work and where to find it – if you can!

- 'Season's Greetings': side of two garages, Port Talbot, Wales

- 'The Mild, Mild West': side of building, Stokes Croft, Bristol

- 'Rage, Flower Thrower': side of a garage, Bethlehem, Palestine

- 'The Grim Reaper': side of a moored boat, Bristol

- 'Washing Zebra Stripes': shattered brick wall, Timbuktu, Mali

- 'Gangsta Rat': Moorfield Eye Hospital, London

- 'There is Always Hope': wall of brick steps, South Bank, London

⟐ FILL IN THE GAP

Read the sentences and choose the correct word or words to fill the gap. Refer back to *Banksy* to find the correct answer.

One of his most famous stencils is '_____', which shows a young girl letting go of a heart-shaped balloon.

Despite the prices paid for his work, many people believe Banksy's art is simple criminal damage because _____ is illegal.

_____ also moved to London around 2000, which is when Banksy's artwork

started appearing there.

⊕ MATCHING

Draw a line with a ruler to match the information.

The Mild, Mild West	•	•	London
Gangsta Rat	•	•	Bethlehem
Washing Zebra Stripes	•	•	Bristol
Rage, Flower Thrower	•	•	Timbuktu

⊘ LABEL

Label the description with the correct information.

2018 price of 'Girl with Balloon'	
city Banksy was born in	
year Banksy was born	
name of book Banksy wrote	
year Banksy made spoof £10 notes	
city where 'Gangsta Rat' art is	

⊙ TRUE OR FALSE

Read the sentences. Put a tick in the correct box to show which sentences are *true* and which are *false*.

'The Mild, Mild West' is one of his most famous stencils.   True ☐   False ☐

Everyone agrees that Banksy's art is a great example for others.   True ☐   False ☐

Banksy printed spoof £10 notes in 2004.   True ☐   False ☐

Banksy's father worked in a bank.   True ☐   False ☐

Many people believe Banksy is Robin Gunningham.   True ☐   False ☐

Comprehension Ninja 9–10 © Andrew Jennings, 2020

◎ MULTIPLE CHOICE

Circle the correct answer to the following question.

What is the title of the Banksy art piece that can be found on the side of a moored boat?

| Season's Greetings | Rage, Flower Thrower | Gangsta Rat | The Grim Reaper |

123 SEQUENCING

Look at *Banksy*. Number the statements from 1 to 4 to show the order they occur in the text.

Many see it as a reflection of children's loss of innocence and people's lack of respect for love.	
Seconds afterwards, a mechanism hidden in its frame shredded it!	
This piece of art was given a new name: 'Love is in the Bin' – and it's believed to be worth at least 50 per cent more now than when it was undamaged.	
The Queen was replaced by Princess Diana's face and they said 'Banksy of England' instead of 'Bank of England'.	

🔍 FIND AND COPY

These questions are about *Banksy*.

Look at the paragraph beginning 'At that point'. Find and copy a word that suggests Bansky's early work was done without stencils.

_____

Look at the paragraph beginning 'You may have seen images'. Find and copy a word that suggests that Banksy thinks children are exposed to too much nowadays.

_____

✒ UNDERLINE OR HIGHLIGHT

Read the paragraph below and then follow the instructions.

People have used these clues to come up with theories about who Banksy really is. The person most commonly believed to be Banksy is Robin Gunningham, an artist who was born in Bristol in 1973. Pictures never show Banksy's face but some contain other details that people believe resemble him.

Underline or highlight a word that means similar to something.

Underline or highlight a word that means ideas that hope to explain a problem.

24 TENZING NORGAY

Mount Everest has always posed a challenge for mountaineers – and many have attempted and failed to climb it. The history books show that the first definitely successful climb was in 1953, by Sir Edmund Hillary and Tenzing Norgay.

Edmund Hillary did the whole climb alongside a Sherpa mountaineer called Tenzing Norgay. Sherpa people are native to the Himalayas in Nepal and were a vital component of any successful ascent up the mountains. They were experienced local climbers who were paid to prepare the route, fix ropes and carry essential kit. Norgay was to become more than just a guide, but also a lifesaver, a history-maker and a friend for life.

Hillary and Norgay's expedition team of 13 Europeans and their guides climbed together to camp 7,890 metres up the mountain – around 1,000 metres from the top. On 26 May, Tom Bourdillon and Charles Evans attempted the climb, but turned back when Evans's oxygen system failed. The pair had come within 91 vertical metres of the summit. The expedition leader Colonel Hunt then directed Norgay and Hillary to try to reach it.

Their ascent was far from easy. Early in the climb, Hillary fell. Norgay reacted quickly, using his ice axe to prevent Hillary from slipping into a crevasse to his death, and enabling him to climb out of the sheer-walled ice chasm. When Hillary was asked about Norgay's heroic actions he answered, 'Tenzing and I were a team. I expected Tenzing to carry out the right procedures in an emergency, just as I would.' From then on, Hillary insisted that he would climb alongside only Norgay.

Finally, on 29 May, Hillary and Norgay made their final push. After having to cut steps up the last frozen rock face, they clambered up – and reached Everest's summit.

Comprehension Ninja 9–10 © Andrew Jennings, 2020

When he was asked about Norgay's reaction, Hillary said:

'Well, Chet Tensing was, I think, on reaching the summit, certainly in many ways more demonstrative than I was. I shook hands with him, rather in British fashion, but this wasn't enough for Tensing. He threw his arms around my shoulders – we were in oxygen masks and all – and he thumped me on the back and I thumped him on the back, and really it was quite a demonstrative moment. And he certainly was very, very thrilled when we reached the summit of Everest.'

After only 15 minutes at the frozen top of the peak, the highest point on Earth, the mountaineers descended to their delighted expedition team. Only days later, back in the Nepalese capital of Kathmandu, Hillary learned that he had been knighted for his achievement. Despite this honour, Hillary was always eager to explain that his was not an achievement that set him apart from his team. He said:

'On this expedition, we had altogether 13 western members of the expedition, and then we had, I think, about 30 permanent high-altitude sherpas. [...] It is a team expedition, and it's very much in the form of a pyramid effort. [...] The two men who reach the summit are completely dependent on the combined effort of all those involved lower down.'

Hillary's greatest praise, though, was always for Norgay. Colonel Hunt agreed; from the moment he was asked who reached the summit first, he'd give the same answer: 'They reached it together. As a team.'

Despite Norgay's part in the achievement, it is often only Hillary who is remembered in the UK. It is clear, however, that Tenzing and Hillary reached Everest's summit together.

⏚ FILL IN THE GAP

Read the sentences and choose the correct word or words to fill the gap. Refer back to
Tenzing Norgay **to find the correct answer.**

Norgay was to become more than just a guide, but also a _____, a history-maker
and a friend for life.

Hillary and Norgay's _____ team of 13 Europeans and their guides climbed
together to camp 7,890 metres up the mountain – around 1,000 metres from the top.

Only days later, back in the Nepalese capital of _____, Hillary learned that he
had been knighted for his achievement.

⏚ MATCHING

Draw a line with a ruler to match the information.

expedition leader
Sherpa mountaineer
failed oxygen system
knighted for his achievement

Charles Evans
Sir Edmund Hillary
Tenzing Norgay
Colonel Hunt

⏚ LABEL

Label the description with the correct date or number.

altitude of the expedition's camp (metres)	
date on which Tom Bourdillon and Charles Evans tried to reach the summit	
vertical distance Bourdillon and Evans were from the summit when they turned back	
date of Tenzing and Hillary's climb to the summit	
time Tenzing and Hillary spent at the summit (minutes)	
number of western members of the team	

⏚ TRUE OR FALSE

Read the sentences. Put a tick in the correct box to show which sentences are *true* and which are *false*.

Norgay prevented Hillary slipping to his death.   True ☐ False ☐

Hillary believed reaching the top was down to teamwork.   True ☐ False ☐

Norgay and Hillary shook hands on reaching the summit.   True ☐ False ☐

The mountaineers descended after 15 minutes.   True ☐ False ☐

Hillary and Norgay made their final push on 29th May.   True ☐ False ☐

◎ MULTIPLE CHOICE

Circle the correct answer to the following question.

Who was the leader of the expedition?

| Sir Edmund Hillary | Tenzing Norgay | Charles Evans | Colonel Hunt |

123 SEQUENCING

Look at *Tenzing Norgay*. Number the statements from 1 to 4 to show the order they occur in the text.

Edmund Hillary did the whole climb alongside a Sherpa mountaineer called Tenzing Norgay.	
Early in the climb, Hillary fell.	
Colonel Hunt agreed; from the moment he was asked who reached the summit first, he'd give the same answer: 'They reached it together. As a team.'	
Their ascent was far from easy.	

⌕ FIND AND COPY

These questions are about *Tenzing Norgay*.

Look at the paragraph beginning 'The ascent was far from easy'. Find and copy a word that suggests Hillary nearly fell into a deep hole in the icy glacier.

_____

Look at the paragraph beginning 'The ascent was far from easy'. Find and copy a word that suggests that Norgay's actions were brave.

_____

◑ UNDERLINE OR HIGHLIGHT

Read the paragraph below and then follow the instructions.

> He threw his arms around my shoulders – we were in oxygen masks and all – and he thumped me on the back and I thumped him on the back, and really it was quite a demonstrative moment. And he certainly was very, very thrilled when we reached the summit of Everest.

Underline or highlight a word that means to freely and openly show affection.

Underline or highlight a word that means extremely pleased.

1. FAIR TRADE

FILL IN THE GAP

1. discrimination
2. treated
3. developing
4. consequence
5. exploit
6. producers
7. businesses
8. clean
9. coffea
10. Kaldi
11. monasteries
12. climate
13. 80 per cent
14. 125 million
15. fair trade

MATCHING

Fair trade focusses on	'developing' countries
Numbers of certified producers	1,411
Goat herder	Kaldi
Close to the equator	coffee belt
Farmers don't have enough	money
Large companies	exploit farmers
Coffee growing region	the coffee belt
Fair trade ensures	everyone treated the same
Paid to fair trade producers	$158.3 million
Fairtrade Foundation logo	guarantee the producer has been paid a fair price
Coffee	a very popular drink
Coffea	a tree
Trade means	buying and selling goods
Fairtrade Foundation logo	green, black and blue
Fair means	equal and without discrimination
Fair trade countries	73
1.66 million	fair trade certified farmers and workers
Energetic goats ate	coffea berries
Small farms produce	80 percent of the world's coffee
Farmers use money for	Clothes, food and medicines

LABEL

1. coffea
2. coffee beans
3. the coffee belt
4. Kaldi
5. coffee
6. buying and selling goods
7. exploited
8. everyone in the world is treated in the same way
9. to keep their businesses
10. the coffee belt
11. small beans
12. fair
13. more than 1.66 million
14. 'developing' countries
15. $158.3 million
16. coffee
17. 73
18. Fairtrade Foundation (logo)

TRUE OR FALSE

1. True
2. True
3. False
4. False
5. False
6. True
7. True
8. False
9. True
10. False
11. True
12. False
13. True
14. False
15. True
16. False
17. False
18. True
19. False
20. False

MULTIPLE CHOICE

everyone is treated the same
buying and selling goods
India, Indonesia, Africa and South America
a tree
exploited
producers
powder of granules
coffea
the coffee belt
a circle

SEQUENCING

1, 3, 2, 5, 4
2, 5, 3, 4, 1
2, 1, 3, 5, 4

FIND AND COPY

equal
developing
communities
profitable
ground
potential
equator

UNDERLINE OR HIGHLIGHT

origins
ancient
noticing
popular
rich
alert

2. MOUNTAINS OF THE WORLD

FILL IN THE GAP

1. picturesque
2. height
3. thousands
4. Alps
5. tectonic plates
6. erupting
7. volcanoes
8. Everest
9. adventurous
10. training
11. Tanzania
12. west
13. symbol
14. snowy
15. active

MATCHING

Fuji	3,776 metres tall
Everest	8,848 metres tall
Kilimanjaro	5,896 metres tall
Vesuvius	1,280 metres tall
Fuji	west of Tokyo
Vesuvius	Italy
Everest	Himalayas
Kilimanjaro	Africa
Nearly 300 people died	Everest
Three inactive volcanoes	Kilimanjaro
Erupted in 79 CE	Vesuvius
Major eruption in 1707	Fuji
Requires intensive training	Everest
Shira is the oldest peak	Kilimanjaro
Classified as active	Fuji
Destroyed Pompeii	Vesuvius
Vesuvius	insight into Roman life
Fuji	conical appearance
Kilimanjaro	three inactive volcanoes
Everest	raise money for charities

LABEL

1. Everest
2. Fuji
3. Vesuvius
4. Fuji
5. Kilimanjaro
6. Vesuvius
7. Fuji
8. Vesuvius
9. Kilimanjaro
10. Kilimanjaro
11. Everest
12. Kilimanjaro
13. Kilimanjaro
14. Everest
15. Kilimanjaro
16. Fuji
17. Vesuvius
18. Vesuvius

TRUE OR FALSE

1.	False	11.	False
2.	True	12.	True
3.	False	13.	False
4.	False	14.	True
5.	True	15.	True
6.	True	16.	True
7.	False	17.	True
8.	True	18.	False
9.	False	19.	False
10.	True	20.	True

MULTIPLE CHOICE

all over the world
a mountain range
the Alps
tectonic plates
8,848 metres
Vesuvius
Naples
more than 50 years
Shira
79 CE

SEQUENCING

3, 1, 2, 5, 4
1, 2, 5, 3, 4
2, 1, 3, 4, 5

FIND AND COPY

picturesque
summit
erupting
queues
overlooking
active
infamous
well preserved

UNDERLINE OR HIGHLIGHT

insight
buried
infamous
incredible
covered
active

3. THE GUNPOWDER PLOT

FILL IN THE GAP

1. fireworks and bonfires
2. parliament
3. doomed
4. Robert Catesby
5. rebellious
6. Earl of Essex
7. suspicion
8. Guido Fawkes
9. 21
10. military
11. Protestant
12. camouflaged
13. plotters'
14. tortured
15. London

MATCHING

Robert Catesby	born around 1572
Warwickshire	Robert Catesby
York	Guy Fawkes
Guy Fawkes	born 1570
Robert Catesby plot to kill	Catholic parents King James I
Guy Fawkes motivated by	Protestant background religion
first rebellion	failed uprising of the Earl of Essex
Catesby dissatisfied with	Protestant rule
arrested by guards	Guy Fawkes
Robert Catesby	suspicion of British government
letter	Lord Monteagle
Guy Fawkes	tortured
Protestant rule	treated Catholics badly
Robert Catesby	head cut off

LABEL

1. Houses of Parliament (in London)
2. Robert Catesby
3. Queen Elizabeth's chief advisor / Robert Cecil
4. Robert Catesby
5. Earl of Essex
6. Queen Elizabeth
7. Guido Fawkes
8. James I
9. Christopher and John Wright and Thomas Winter
10. Lord Monteagle
11. London
12. Staffordshire
13. Guy Fawkes / Guido Fawkes
14. London
15. Across Great Britain
16. the plotters
17. (Guy) Fawkes
18. (Guy) Fawkes

TRUE OR FALSE

1.	True	9.	True
2.	False	10.	False
3.	False	11.	True
4.	True	12.	False
5.	False	13.	True
6.	False	14.	True
7.	True	15.	False
8.	True		

MULTIPLE CHOICE

5 November
Robert Catesby
Guido Fawkes
Robert Catesby
1604
Houses of Parliament
King James I
London
Staffordshire
death

SEQUENCING

2, 3, 5, 4, 1
1, 5, 3, 4, 2
2, 4, 5, 1, 3

FIND AND COPY

significant
doomed
motivated
differences
rebellious
failed
converted
dissatisfied

UNDERLINE OR HIGHLIGHT

treason
public
tortured
accomplice(s)
gunpowder
execution

4. QUEEN VICTORIA

FILL IN THE GAP

1. throne
2. reigned
3. Kensington Palace
4. Kent
5. protective
6. play
7. 132
8. diary
9. character
10. King William IV
11. Westminster Abbey
12. Buckingham Palace
13. declined
14. nine
15. invented

MATCHING

Queen Victoria's birthplace	Kensington Palace
reigned for	over 60 years
Victoria born	May 1819
Queen Victoria died	January 1901
mother	Victoria Mary Louisa
dog	Dash
father	Prince Edward
mother and father known as	Duke and Duchess of Kent
mother	strict rules
dolls	132
enjoyed	painting
kept a	diary
known as	the Grandmother of Europe
as a baby	fifth in line for throne
Buckingham Palace	first monarch
spent Christmas at	Osborne House
Queen Victoria's son	King Edward VII
Queen Victoria's age when Prince Albert died	42
Prince Albert died	1861
number of children	9

LABEL

1. more than 60 years
2. (24 May) 1819
3. 132
4. 1837
5. 1839
6. 18
7. 1861
8. 42
9. nine / 9
10. 17
11. 1901
12. 81
13. Osborne House
14. Canada, Australia and India
15. Westminster Abbey
16. Buckingham Palace
17. Kensington Palace
18. Kent

TRUE OR FALSE

1. False
2. False
3. False
4. False
5. False
6. False
7. True
8. False
9. True
10. True
11. True
12. False
13. True
14. True
15. False
16. True
17. False
18. True
19. True
20. True

MULTIPLE CHOICE

over 60 years
81
nine
cousin

King William IV
Grandmother of Europe
Manchester, Leeds and Birmingham
King Edward VII
1861
Osborne House

SEQUENCING

3, 2, 4, 5, 1
5, 2, 3, 4, 1
1, 2, 4, 3, 5

FIND AND COPY

reigned
strict
loneliness
lengthy
unlikely
lavish
proposed
declined

UNDERLINE OR HIGHLIGHT

expansion
rarely
distribution
colonies
related

5. THE CIRCULATORY SYSTEM

FILL IN THE GAP

1. complex network
2. circulatory
3. carbon dioxide
4. heart
5. four
6. atria
7. contracts
8. capillaries
9. routes
10. five litres
11. oxygen
12. waste
13. 20 seconds
14. United Kingdom
15. donate

MATCHING

the heart	muscle
the blood vessels	small tubes
blood volume	five litres
circulatory system	three main parts
contracts	squeezes
the blood	white blood cells
arteries	blood containing oxygen
the heart	four chambers
veins	blood containing carbon dioxide
capillaries	connectors
the heart	atria and ventricles
the blood	platelets and plasma
plasma transports	proteins
blood types	A, B, AB and O
age to donate blood in the UK	17
upper chambers	vetricles
platelets	cause clotting
most common blood group	O
plasma	transports nutrients
lower chambers	ventricles

LABEL

1. the circulatory system
2. the heart
3. the circulatory system
4. blood
5. platelets
6. white blood cells
7. blood
8. arteries
9. plasma
10. ventricles
11. capillaries
12. heart
13. blood
14. heart
15. veins
16. A, B, AB and O
17. 17
18. atria

TRUE OR FALSE

1. False
2. True
3. False
4. False
5. True
6. True
7. False
8. True
9. True
10. False
11. True
12. True
13. True
14. True
15. True

MULTIPLE CHOICE

plasma
A, B, AB and O
O
platelets
red blood cells
white blood cells
five litres
veins
arteries
lungs

SEQUENCING

3, 1, 2, 5, 4
3, 5, 4, 2, 1
1, 5, 2, 4, 3

FIND AND COPY

cycle
repeatedly
contracts
collects
network
attack
vital
donate

UNDERLINE OR HIGHLIGHT

transported
astonishingly
components
common
infections

6. ORDNANCE SURVEY MAPS

FILL IN THE GAP

1. military supplies
2. rebellion
3. French Revolution
4. detailed
5. William Roy
6. man-made
7. eight
8. topographers
9. trenches
10. 20 million
11. artillery targets
12. high
13. slopes
14. symbols
15. campsites

MATCHING

Ordnance Survey	owned by the government
Scottish rebellion	1745
Ordnance Survey maps	extremely detailed
maps record	information about car parks
William Roy	21 years old
distance measured using	chains
survey of Scotland	eight years to complete
Roy's team	eight people
mapped during war	trenches and batteries
significant role in	World War I and II campaigns
90 per cent of war maps in Britain	Ordnance Survey produced
Ordnance Survey supplies	20 million maps
extremely details maps of	roads, forests, parks and rivers
primary role	accurately assess the distance of enemy targets
died during World War I	67 members of Ordnance Survey
contour lines	show how high land is
close contour lines	sharply sloping land
replaced words	symbols
symbols	youth hostels, campsites or bus stations
explains symbols	key

LABEL

1. south of England
2. France
3. Great Britain
4. (Britain's) World War I and World War II (campaigns)
5. 1915 (onwards)
6. 1745
7. 21
8. 800
9. 1915
10. 90 (per cent)
11. 67
12. 20 million
13. war effort
14. contour lines
15. Great Map
16. eight years
17. symbols
18. key

TRUE OR FALSE

1. True
2. True
3. True
4. False
5. False
6. True
7. False
8. True
9. True
10. True
11. True
12. True
13. True
14. False
15. False

MULTIPLE CHOICE

symbols
steep land
67
assess distances
20 million
over 800 people
both World Wars
key
21
southern coasts

SEQUENCING

5, 4, 3, 1, 2
3, 1, 4, 5, 2
4, 5, 1, 2, 3

FIND AND COPY

changing
rebellion
man-made
team
trained
tirelessly
primary
innovative

UNDERLINE OR HIGHLIGHT

campaigns
role
allies
plotting
tirelessly
trenches

7. EUROPEAN CULTURE

FILL IN THE GAP

1. continent
2. traditions
3. architecture
4. Kurdish
5. classical musicians
6. Ludwig van Beethoven
7. Sport
8. world-famous
9. Vikings
10. government
11. Danes'
12. mythical
13. sun-ripened
14. Colosseum

MATCHING

German culture	Polish, Kurdish and Danish languages
Danish culture	Viking links
Greek culture	Zeus and Hades
Europe	a continent
Greek culture	Trojan War
Danish culture	arts, theatre and culture
German culture	classical musicians
the Parthenon	Greece
olive oil	Greek culture
cycling	Danish culture
motor sports	German culture
Houses of Parliament	London
Danish culture	government funding for the arts
Greek culture	Mediterranean sea
German culture	Beethoven and Bach
symbol of culture	the Colosseum, Rome
Theseus	Minotaur
Paris	the Louvre
royal family	London
exported food	sausages

LABEL

1. Danish
2. Greek
3. German
4. Greek
5. Greek
6. French
7. Germany
8. United Kingdom
9. Denmark
10. Greece
11. Italy
12. France
13. sausages and beer
14. Odense
15. over 40
16. Formula 1 World Championships
17. Trojan War
18. United Kingdom

TRUE OR FALSE

1. False
2. True
3. False
4. True
5. True
6. False
7. False
8. True
9. True
10. False
11. False
12. True
13. True
14. False
15. True

MULTIPLE CHOICE

over 40
1954
German
Danish
11
USA
Colosseum
Greek
Danish
German

SEQUENCING

2, 1, 5, 4, 3
4, 1, 5, 2, 3
3, 4, 1, 2, 5

FIND AND COPY

divided
recognisable
composers
exported
annual
raided
guarded
illustrates

UNDERLINE OR HIGHLIGHT

official
delicious
celebrated
native
exported
musician

8. PLANETS IN THE SOLAR SYSTEM

FILL IN THE GAP

eight
explored
moon
closest
acidic
opposite
orbit
iron
ten
spacecraft
62
the Sun
Neptune
discovery
properties

MATCHING

Mercury	closest to the sun
Earth	fifth largest planet
Mars	iron
Saturn	hydrogen and helium
Venus	hottest planet
Jupiter	largest planet
Uranus	four times wider than Earth
Neptune	not visible to the naked eye
discovered 1846	Neptune
red planet	Mars
79 moons in total	Jupiter
62 moons in total	Saturn
destroy any vehicle	Jupiter
165 years to orbit the Sun	Neptune
smallest planet	Mercury
spins in opposite direction to Earth	Venus
Earth	365 days to orbit the Sun
solar system	eight planets
Mercury	88 Earth days to orbit the Sun
Saturn	rings of ice and rock

LABEL

1. Mercury
2. Jupiter
3. Mars
4. Jupiter
5. Neptune
6. Uranus
7. Uranus
8. Saturn
9. Mars
10. Earth
11. Mars
12. Saturn
13. Jupiter
14. Venus
15. Neptune
16. Neptune
17. Uranus
18. Saturn

TRUE OR FALSE

1. True
2. False
3. False
4. True
5. False
6. False
7. True
8. False
9. False
10. False
11. True
12. False
13. True
14. True
15. True

MULTIPLE CHOICE

Mercury
Mars
Neptune
Uranus
Earth
eight
Mars
Jupiter
Uranus
Venus

SEQUENCING

2, 3, 4, 1, 5
5, 1, 4, 3, 2
1, 5, 3, 2, 4

FIND AND COPY

experts
orbit
unusually
inhabited
extinct
similar
uniquely
properties

UNDERLINE OR HIGHLIGHT

feature
completed
distant
support
believed
rotation

9. THE BLACK DEATH

FILL IN THE GAP

1. Finland and Iceland's
2. remoteness
3. Europe
4. isolate
5. bitten
6. swellings
7. colonies
8. rat
9. Italian
10. clothing
11. trade routes
12. infectious
13. bacteria
14. culprits
15. lived
16. China

MATCHING

real culprits	fleas
believed that bacteria circulated by	black rats
bacteria	yersinia pestis
lived in sewers and cellars	grey and brown rats
lived on black rats	fleas
fleas embedded in	human clothing
lived close to humans	black rats
black rats	travelled on ships
plague origin	China
Black Death	bubonic plague
Mongol army	attacked Italian trading post
fleas' preferred food source	black rats
once all rats died	fleas began to bite humans
died after ten to 14 days	infected rat colonies
three to five days after being bitten	humans fall ill
infected humans had	painful swellings
deaths in Europe	75-200 million people
escaped the plague	Iceland and Finland
bacteria spread quickly	warmer temperatures
killed bacteria	freezing temperatures

LABEL

1. yersinia pestis
2. black rats
3. fleas
4. grey and brown rats
5. 75-200 million (people)
6. the Black Death
7. the 1300s
8. human clothing
9. China
10. Crimea
11. ten to 14 days
12. humans
13. painful swellings
14. three to five days
15. buboes
16. isolating people
17. Iceland and Finland
18. freezing (temperatures)

TRUE OR FALSE

1. True
2. False
3. False
4. True
5. True
6. True
7. True
8. False
9. False
10. False
11. True
12. False
13. False
14. True
15. False

MULTIPLE CHOICE

black rats
close to humans
fleas
clothes
China
three to five days
isolation / isolate
Finland and Iceland
30 to 60 per cent
freezing temperatures

SEQUENCING

2, 3, 4, 5, 1
3, 1, 4, 5, 2
4, 1, 3, 2, 5

FIND AND COPY

estimate
spread
passed
flourishing
retreated
isolate
untouched
remoteness

UNDERLINE OR HIGHLIGHT

voyages
retreated
flourishing
survive
aboard
vessels

10. MENTAL HEALTH

FILL IN THE GAP

1. cope
2. 21st century
3. creep
4. realise
5. nature
6. vitamin D
7. chemicals
8. experiences
9. mental health
10. patients
11. mental health
12. relentlessly
13. Depression
14. weight
15. Anxiety
16. Endorphins

MATCHING

anxiety	feeling of fear or panic
depression	having an extremely low mood
OCD	repeating thoughts
eating disorder	worry about weight
eating disorder	girls are ten times more likely to suffer
anxiety	8.2 million UK cases in 2013
depression	avoid activity
OCD	obsessions
common type of mental illness	depression
washing the hands many times	OCD
try to lose weight	eating disorder
one in six young people	anxiety
'happy' chemicals	endorphins
first step	speaking to someone you trust
mental health charity	Mind
sun	vitamin D
cause of poor mental health	emotional trauma
2018 survey	74 per cent of people felt stressed
mental health problems	can affect anyone
stop isolation	shared experiences

LABEL

1. anxiety
2. OCD / Obsessive-compulsive disorder
3. depression
4. anorexia / bulimia
5. anxiety
6. eating disorders
7. 74 (per cent)
8. endorphins
9. Mind
10. exercising
11. (vitamin) D
12. plants and animals
13. anxiety
14. mental health problems
15. OCD / Obsessive-compulsive disorder
16. eating disorders
17. depression
18. OCD / Obsessive-compulsive disorder

TRUE OR FALSE

1. True
2. True
3. True
4. False
5. True
6. True
7. False
8. False
9. True
10. False
11. True
12. True
13. True
14. False
15. True

MULTIPLE CHOICE

21st century
anxiety
depression
bulimia
2018
doctors
exercise
sun
Mind
OCD

SEQUENCING

2, 3, 1, 4, 5
5, 1, 2, 3, 4
1, 2, 3, 4, 5

FIND AND COPY

cope
rise
inherited
overwhelmed
nervous
persistent
avoid
repeating

UNDERLINE OR HIGHLIGHT

related
reported
logical
disorders
panic
prolonged

11. RECYCLING

FILL IN THE GAP

1. Recycling
2. Repair
3. Re-use
4. Denmark
5. cotton buds
6. rewards
7. Refill
8. illegally
9. metal objects
10. Refuse
11. flatten
12. degrade
13. Reduce
14. landfill
15. 1,000

MATCHING

flatten	cardboard boxes
reduce	plastic
landfill	site for dumping rubbish
crush	cans
recycling	turning waste into new products
refuse	don't buy things you don't need
reduce landfill waste	paperless billing
check recycling day	council
micro-beads	banned by the UK government
easily recycled	most paper and cardboard
refill	bottles, travel cups and food containers
reverse vending machines	Denmark
blown into the sea	plastic litter
plastic waste	eaten by animals
refunds money for bottles	reverse vending machine
re-use	donate clothes or save carrier bags
methane	most serious gas
repair	if something breaks, fix it
degrade and rot	landfill contents
landfill	created gases

LABEL

1. recycling
2. landfill sites
3. gases
4. methane
5. energy (and fewer resources)
6. non-recycled waste
7. cardboard boxes
8. the sea
9. millions of tonnes
10. micro-beads
11. Denmark
12. nearly 3,000
13. re-use
14. refuse
15. reduce
16. repair
17. re-use
18. refill

TRUE OR FALSE

1. True
2. True
3. False
4. False
5. False
6. False
7. True
8. True
9. True
10. False
11. True
12. True
13. False
14. False
15. True

MULTIPLE CHOICE

landfill
gases
methane
1,000
wind and rain
micro-beads
animals' habitats
Denmark
Germany
five

SEQUENCING

5, 1, 2, 4, 3
1, 2, 5, 3, 4
4, 1, 2, 5, 3

FIND AND COPY

used / waste
preserve
designated
degrade / rot
illegally
reduce
refunding
reusable

UNDERLINE OR HIGHLIGHT

customer
innovations
paperless
refunding
reverse
returned

12. THE TOUR DE FRANCE

FILL IN THE GAP

1.	under 26	9.	thirty
2.	yellow jersey	10.	better suited
3.	difficult hills	11.	specialist
4.	most points	12.	Chris Froome
5.	conviction	13.	high-profile
6.	oxygen	14.	sprawling cities
7.	invalidated	15.	200 cyclists
8.	cheating		

MATCHING

Bradley Wiggins	Olympic gold medal winner
Philippa York	King of the Mountain
Mark Cavendish	specialist sprinter
Tour de France	world's most famous race

Giro d'Italia 2018	Chris Froome
MBE 2011	Mark Cavendish
July 1903	first race
Tour de France 2012	Bradley Wiggins

Chris Froome	2013
Jacques Anquetil	1957
Greg LeMond	1990
Mark Cavendish	never won

Lance Armstrong	seven Tour de France titles invalidated
green jersey	most points
EPO	produces more red blood cells
polka-dot jersey	best climber
yellow jersey	lowest total time
admitted cheating on TV	Lance Armstrong
banned drug	EPO
white jersey	best rider under 26

LABEL

1.	Miguel Indurain	10.	green jersey
2.	Mark Canvendish	11.	white jersey
3.	Philippa York	12.	Greg LeMond
4.	Bradley Wiggins	13.	Phillipe Thys
5.	Lance Armstrong	14.	Miguel Indurain
6.	Jacques Anquetil	15.	Eddy Merckx
7.	yellow jersey	16.	Louison Bobet
8.	polka-dot jersey	17.	Bernard Hinault
9.	yellow jersey		

TRUE OR FALSE

1.	True	9.	True
2.	False	10.	False
3.	False	11.	True
4.	False	12.	False
5.	True	13.	True
6.	True	14.	False
7.	True	15.	True
8.	True		

MULTIPLE CHOICE

July
22
Paris
1903
white
polka-dot
Greg LeMond
Miguel Indurain
Lance Armstrong
red blood cells

SEQUENCING

2, 4, 3, 5, 1
3, 1, 2, 5, 4
2, 4, 1, 3, 5

FIND AND COPY

compete
epic
accumulated
steep
bronze
rocked
invalidated
prolific

UNDERLINE OR HIGHLIGHT

glory
denying
admitted
resilience
(performance-) enhancing
cheating

13. THE BRITISH EMPIRE

FILL IN THE GAP

British colonies
influence
United States

MATCHING

Captain James Cook	claimed Australia for Britain
British East India Company	drove Britain's influence
British Empire	covered over six times more land than the Roman Empire
Hudson's Bay Company	created in Canada

LABEL

1960
1920
1670
1776
1770
1807

TRUE OR FALSE

1.	True	4.	False
2.	True	5.	True
3.	False		

MULTIPLE CHOICE

over 3.5 million

SEQUENCING

4, 2, 3, 1

FIND AND COPY

profitable
voluntarily

UNDERLINE OR HIGHLIGHT

regained
achieved

14. J.K. ROWLING

FILL IN THE GAP

seven
translated
Lifetime

MATCHING

J.K. Rowling born	near Bristol
taught English	Portugal
relocated to	Edinburgh
had the idea	on a train

LABEL

2016
2018
2012
2007
over 75
12

TRUE OR FALSE

True
True
True
False
False

MULTIPLE CHOICE

2.65 million

SEQUENCING

1, 4, 2, 3

FIND AND COPY

passion
collaborated

UNDERLINE OR HIGHLIGHT

cult
pseudonym

15. RESIDENTIAL ACTIVITIES

FILL IN THE GAP

symbols
coordination
harness

MATCHING

targets at a distance	archery
balance, rhythm and determination	kayaking
requires a harness	zip lines
combines fitness and fun	orienteering

LABEL

bushcraft
crate climbing
kayaking
night line
orienteering
abseiling

TRUE OR FALSE

1. True
2. True
3. False
4. True
5. False

MULTIPLE CHOICE

five stars

SEQUENCING

1, 4, 3, 2

FIND AND COPY

adrenaline-filled
collapse

UNDERLINE OR HIGHLIGHT

gained
navigation

16. ICEBERGS

FILL IN THE GAP

glaciers
catastrophe
trickle

MATCHING

iceberg creation process	calving
icebergs the size of cars	growlers
icebergs the size of houses	bergy bits
the shape of an iceberg	'tabular' or 'non-tabular'

LABEL

ships
tabular
non-tabular
glaciers (and other ice structures)
freshwater
Iceberg Alley

TRUE OR FALSE

1. False
2. False
3. True
4. True
5. False

MULTIPLE CHOICE

New York

SEQUENCING

2, 1, 4, 3

FIND AND COPY

catastrophe / disaster
misleading

UNDERLINE OR HIGHLIGHT

extravagant
avoid

17. RAINFOREST ANIMALS

FILL IN THE GAP

nutrient-rich
apex predators
Piranhas

MATCHING

harpy eagle	Harpia hapyja
emerald tree boa	Corallus caninus
sloth	Folivora
piranha	Pygocentrus nattereri

LABEL

harpy eagle
sloth
piranhas
emerald tree boa
emerald tree boa
harpy eagle

TRUE OR FALSE

1. False
2. False
3. True
4. False
5. True

MULTIPLE CHOICE

sloth

SEQUENCING

2, 3, 1, 4

FIND AND COPY

solitary
drastic

UNDERLINE OR HIGHLIGHT

plentiful
gauged

18. GRAVITY

FILL IN THE GAP

planets
Moon
apple tree

MATCHING

ancient Greek philosopher	Aristotle
an invisible force	gravity
discovered gravity	Newton
famous book	Philosophiæ Naturalis Principia Mathematica

LABEL

gravity
gravitational pull of the Moon
their weight
apple
the National Trust
Newton-metre

TRUE OR FALSE

1. True
2. False
3. False
4. True
5. True

MULTIPLE CHOICE

384-322 BCE

SEQUENCING

2, 4, 1, 3

FIND AND COPY

comfortable
legacy

UNDERLINE OR HIGHLIGHT

invisible
discuss

19. COUNTRY STUDY: AUSTRALIA

FILL IN THE GAP

Sydney
Melbourne
New South Wales

MATCHING

koalas, kangaroos and platypuses	inhabitants
Dutch explorers landed in 1606	history
Uluru	geography
beaches and barbecues	Australian stereotypes

LABEL

Great Barrier Reef
1901
36
Melbourne
Canberra
gold

TRUE OR FALSE

1. True
2. False
3. True
4. False
5. True

MULTIPLE CHOICE

Canberra

SEQUENCING

2, 1, 4, 3

FIND AND COPY

populated
settled

UNDERLINE OR HIGHLIGHT

diverse / range
remote

20. MOSQUES

FILL IN THE GAP

Medina
fountains
disrespectful

MATCHING

festival	Ramadan
holiest place in Islam	Ka'aba
Medina	Prophet Mohammed
tall towers on mosques	minarets

LABEL

prayer halls
shoe rack
washing / wudu
seats
mihrab
dome / qubba

TRUE OR FALSE

1.	True	4.	True
2.	False	5.	True
3.	True		

MULTIPLE CHOICE

5 per cent

SEQUENCING

1, 2, 3, 4

FIND AND COPY

prevent
accommodate

UNDERLINE OR HIGHLIGHT

traditionally
paradise

21. WOLVES

FILL IN THE GAP

alpha
wolves
killing

MATCHING

Yellowstone National Park	reintroduced grey wolves
no eye contact	alpha wolf
literature	bad-guy wolf
live mostly in Asia	Indian wolves

LABEL

Indian wolves
red wolves
Himalayan wolves
Arctic wolves
Ethiopian wolves
grey wolves

TRUE OR FALSE

1.	False	4.	True
2.	False	5.	True
3.	False		

MULTIPLE CHOICE

grey wolf

SEQUENCING

4, 3, 2, 1

FIND AND COPY

reintroduced
dwindling

UNDERLINE OR HIGHLIGHT

centuries
cunning / trickster

22. GERMS: UNWANTED INVADERS

FILL IN THE GAP

saliva
measles
smallpox

MATCHING

milkmaids rarely caught	smallpox
Jenner infected	James Phipps
never forget chemical codes	white blood cells
Edward Jenner	father of immunology

LABEL

Edward Jenner
James Phipps
milkmaids
vaccines
white blood cells
germs

TRUE OR FALSE

1.	True	4.	True
2.	True	5.	False
3.	True		

MULTIPLE CHOICE

smallpox

SEQUENCING

2, 4, 3, 1

FIND AND COPY

immune
fatal

UNDERLINE OR HIGHLIGHT

theory
mild

23. BANKSY

FILL IN THE GAP

Girl with Balloon
graffiti
Gunningham

MATCHING

The Mild, Milk West	Bristol
Gangsta Rat	London
Washing Zebra Stripes	Timbuktu
Rage, Flower Thrower	Bethlehem

LABEL

£1 million
Bristol
1974
Wall and Piece
2004
London

TRUE OR FALSE

1.	False	4.	False
2.	False	5.	True
3.	True		

MULTIPLE CHOICE

The Grim Reaper

SEQUENCING

1, 2, 3, 4

FIND AND COPY

freehand
innocence

UNDERLINE OR HIGHLIGHT

resemble
clues

24. TENZING NORGAY

FILL IN THE GAP

lifesaver
expedition
Kathmandu

MATCHING

expedition leader	Colonel Hunt
Sherpa mountaineer	Tenzing Norgay
failed oxygen system	Charles Evans
knighted for his achievement	Sir Edmund Hillary

LABEL

7,890 (metres)
26 May
91 (vertical metres)
29 May
15 (minutes)
13

TRUE OR FALSE

1.	True	4.	True
2.	True	5.	True
3.	True		

MULTIPLE CHOICE

Colonel Hunt

SEQUENCING

1, 3, 4, 2

FIND AND COPY

crevasse / (ice) chasm
heroic

UNDERLINE OR HIGHLIGHT

demonstrative
thrilled